3923

Blairsville Junior High School
Blairsville, Pennsylvania

THE BIRDS AND THE BEASTS WERE THERE

Also edited by William Cole

POEMS FOR SEASONS AND CELEBRATIONS

POEMS OF MAGIC AND SPELLS

I WENT TO THE ANIMAL FAIR

STORY POEMS NEW AND OLD

HUMOROUS POETRY FOR CHILDREN

BEASTLY BOYS AND GHASTLY GIRLS

The Birds and the Beasts Were There

ANIMAL POEMS SELECTED BY

WILLIAM COLE

Woodcuts by Helen Siegl

THE WORLD PUBLISHING COMPANY
Cleveland and New York

Published by The World Publishing Company
2231 West 110th Street, Cleveland 2, Ohio

Published simultaneously in Canada by
Nelson, Foster & Scott Ltd.

Library of Congress Catalog Card Number: 63-18467

MWP

Copyright © 1963 by William Cole
All rights reserved. No part of this book may be reproduced in any form without written permission from the publisher, except for brief passages included in a review appearing in a newspaper or magazine. Printed in the United States of America.

COPYRIGHT ACKNOWLEDGMENTS

The editor and The World Publishing Company herewith render thanks to the following authors, publishers, and agents whose interest, co-operation, and permission to reprint have made possible the preparation of *The Birds and the Beasts Were There.* All possible care has been taken to trace the ownership of every selection included and to make full acknowledgment for its use. If any errors have accidentally occurred, they will be corrected in subsequent editions, provided notification is sent to the publishers.

Marnie Pomeroy Ackerman, for her poems "Chipmunks," "Ground Hog Day," and "The Opossum." Reprinted by permission of the author.

Angus and Robertson Ltd., for excerpt from "Swans at Night" by Mary Gilmore from *Modern Australian Poetry,* published by Melbourne University Press. Reprinted by permission of Angus and Robertson Ltd.

Harry Behn, for his poem "Deer" from *Sombra,* published by Christtreu. Reprinted by permission of the author.

Elizabeth Coatsworth Beston, for "Concrete Trap" by Elizabeth Coatsworth from *The Saturday Review,* 1934. Reprinted by permission of Elizabeth Coatsworth Beston and *The Saturday Review.*

The Bodley Head Ltd., for "Diamond Cut Diamond" from *Diamond Cut Diamond* by Ewart Milne. Reprinted by permission of The Bodley Head Ltd.

Milton Bracker, for his poem "Ballade of a Zoo Buff." Reprinted by permission of the author.

Jonathan Cape Ltd., for excerpt from *The Flaming Terrapin* by Roy Campbell. Reprinted by permission of Jonathan Cape Ltd.

Doris Cohen, for "Prayer to Go to Paradise with the Donkeys" by Francis Jammes (translated by Alan Conder) from *Love,* edited by Walter de la Mare, 1946, William Morrow & Company. Reprinted by permission of Doris Cohen.

Peggy Bennett Cole, for her poems "Bird Thou Never Wert," "Greed," "Lord of Jesters, Prince of Fellows," "Over the Green Sands," "Pearls Among Swine," "Plain Talk for a Pachyderm," "Rose's Calf," "A Snap Judgment of the Llama," "Tatterdemalion," and "Truth Will Out." Reprinted by permission of the author.

Padraic Colum, for his poem "River-Mates." Reprinted by permission of the author.

Coward-McCann, Inc., for "The Mouse" from *Compass Rose* by Elizabeth Coatsworth, copyright, 1929 ®, 1957, Elizabeth Coatsworth. Reprinted by permission of Coward-McCann, Inc.

The Cresset Press Ltd., for "Country Idyll" and "Night Song" from *Collected Poems* by Frances Cornford, 1954; for "The Bat" from *Urania* by Ruth Pitter, 1950. Reprinted by permission of The Cresset Press Ltd.

Curtis Brown Ltd., London, for "The Zebras" from *Adamaster* by Roy Campbell, 1931. Reprinted by permission of Curtis Brown Ltd. on behalf of Estate Roy Campbell.

Geoffrey Dearmer, for his poem "The Turkish Trench Dog." Reprinted by permission of the author.

J. M. Dent & Sons Ltd., for excerpt from "Meeting" from *First Day* by Clifford Dyment. Reprinted by permission of J. M. Dent & Sons Ltd.

Andre Deutsch Ltd., for "The Rhinoceros" from *The Idle Demon* by R. P. Lister. Reprinted by permission of Andre Deutsch Ltd.

The Devin-Adair Company, for "Monkeys" from *Collected Poems* by Padraic Colum, published by The Devin-Adair Company, revised edition October, 1953. Reprinted by permission of The Devin-Adair Company.

The Dolphin Publishing Company Ltd., for "Conversion" from *Life Through Young Eyes* by J. T. Lillie, 1960. Reprinted by permission of The Dolphin Publishing Company Ltd.

Doubleday & Company, Inc., for "the flattered lightning bug," "pete at the seashore," and "short course in natural history," from *Archy and Mehitabel* by Don Marquis, copyright, 1927, Doubleday & Company, Inc.; for "The Bat," copyright, 1938, 1939, "The Heron," copyright, 1937, "The Sloth," copyright, 1950, "Snake," copyright © 1955, Theodore Roethke from *Words for the Wind* by Theodore Roethke. Reprinted by permission of Doubleday & Company, Inc.

Peter Kane Dufault, for his poem "Horse and Hammer." Reprinted by permission of the author.

Gerald Duckworth & Co. Ltd., for "Milk for the Cat" from *Collected Poems* by Harold Monro. Reprinted by permission of Gerald Duckworth & Co. Ltd.

E. P. Dutton & Company, Inc., for "The Ambiguous Dog" and "The Dog's Cold Nose" from *Lyric Laughter* by Arthur Guiterman, copyright, 1939, E. P. Dutton & Co., Inc.; for "Mule Song" from *Gaily the Troubadour* by Arthur Guiterman, copyright, 1936, E. P. Dutton & Co., Inc.; for "The Bat" from *Death and General Putnam and 101 Other Poems* by Arthur Guiterman, copyright, 1935, E. P. Dutton & Co., Inc., Renewal, 1963, Mrs. Arthur Guiterman; for "The Hunt" from *Declensions of the Air* by Louis Kent, copyright, 1950, E. P. Dutton & Co., Inc.; for "The Snowy Owl" from *Pauses of the Eve* by Ernest Kroll, copyright, 1955, Ernest Kroll; for "Life" from *Selected Poems* by Alfred Kreymborg, copyright, 1945, Alfred Kreymborg. Reprinted by permission of E. P. Dutton & Co., Inc.

E. P. Dutton & Co., Inc. and William Heinemann Ltd., for "The Catipoce," "The Doze," "Let No One Suppose," and "The Nonny" from *Prefabulous Animiles* by James Reeves, copyright © 1957, James Reeves and Edward Ardizzone; for "The Four Horses" and "The Snail" from *The Wandering Moon* by James Reeves. Reprinted by permission of E. P. Dutton & Co., Inc. and William Heinemann Ltd.

E. P. Dutton & Co., Inc. and Oxford University Press, for "Cows" and "Mick" from *The Blackbird in the Lilac* by James Reeves. Reprinted by permission of E. P. Dutton & Co., Inc. and Oxford University Press.

Norma Millay Ellis, for "The Fawn" and "The Rabbit" from *Collected Poems* by Edna St. Vincent Millay, copyright, "The Fawn," 1934, 1962, Edna St. Vincent Millay and Norma Millay Ellis; "The Rabbit," 1939, Edna St. Vincent Millay, published by Harper & Bros. Reprinted by permission of Norma Millay Ellis.

Bruce Fearing, for his poem "Some Brown Sparrows" from *The Beat Scene,* published by Corinth Books, Inc., copyright, 1960, Fred McDarrah and Elias Wilentz. Reprinted by permission of the author.

The Fine Editions Press, for "Of Foxes" by B. Y. Williams from *The Poetry Society of America Anthology.* Reprinted by permission of The Fine Editions Press.

Hugh Finn, for his poem "Beetle" from *New Poems, 1954,* published by P. E. N. International. Reprinted by permission of the author.

Mrs. Arthur Guiterman, for "Song of Hate for Eels" by Arthur Guiterman. Reprinted by permission of Mrs. Arthur Guiterman.

Harcourt, Brace & World, Inc., for "crazy jay blue)" from *95 Poems* © 1958, E. E. Cummings, for "r-p-o-p-h-e-s-s-a-g-r," copyright, 1935, E. E. Cummings, renewed, © 1963, Marion Morehouse Cummings, from *Poems 1923-54* by E. E. Cummings; for "Orchard" from *In an Iridescent Time,* © 1959, Ruth Stone. Reprinted by permission of Harcourt, Brace & World, Inc.

Harcourt, Brace & World, Inc. and Faber & Faber Ltd., for "Macavity: The Mystery Cat" from *Old Possum's Book of Practical Cats,* copyright, 1939, T. S. Eliot. Reprinted by permission of Harcourt, Brace & World, Inc. and Faber & Faber Ltd.

Harper & Row, Publishers, Inc., for "Biddy," "Litter of Pigs," and "Sheep Shearing" from *Barnyard Year* by Fred Lape, copyright, 1950, Fred Lape. Reprinted by permission of Harper & Row, Publishers, Inc.

Harper & Row, Publishers, Inc. and Faber & Faber Ltd., for "Bullfrog" from *Lupercal* by Ted Hughes, copyright, 1960, Ted Hughes. Reprinted by permission of Harper & Row, Publishers, Inc. and Faber & Faber Ltd.

Rupert Hart-Davis Ltd., for "A Blackbird Singing" by R. S. Thomas from *Poetry for Supper;* for "January" by R. S. Thomas from *Song at the Year's End;* for "A Dead Mole," "A Dead Bird," and "The Swallows" from *The Collected Poems of Andrew Young.* Reprinted by permission of Rupert Hart-Davis Ltd.

David Higham Associates, Inc., for "Lullaby for a Baby Toad" from *Collected Poems* by Stella Gibbons, published by Longmans, Green & Company Ltd. Reprinted by permission of David Higham Associates.

Holt, Rinehart & Winston, Inc., for "A Considerable Speck," "The Pasture," and "The Runaway" from *Complete Poems of Robert Frost,* copyright, 1923, 1930, 1939, Holt, Rinehart & Winston, Inc., copyright, 1942, Robert Frost, copyright renewed, 1951, Robert Frost; for "Questioning Faces" from *In the Clearing* by Robert Frost, copyright, © 1962, Robert Frost. Reprinted by permission of Holt, Rinehart & Winston, Inc.

Houghton Mifflin Company, for "The Sandhill Crane" from *The Children Sing in the Far West* by Mary Austin; for "The Fish" from *North and South* by Elizabeth Bishop; for "The Masked Shrew" from *Birthdays from the Ocean* by Isabella Gardner; for "White Season" from *Pool in the Meadow* by Frances M.

Frost; for "The Dormouse" from *The Snow Rabbit* by Pati Hill. Reprinted by permission of Houghton Mifflin Company.

Mary Kennedy, for her poems "The Hummingbird" and "To Three Small Rabbits in a Burrow." Reprinted by permission of the author.

Alfred A. Knopf, Inc., for untitled poem from *James and the Giant Peach* by Roald Dahl, copyright, © 1961, by Roald Dahl; for "Bobwhite" and "Moo!" from *Collected Poems* by Robert Hillyer, copyright, © 1961, Robert Hillyer; for "Mallard" from *Poems and Contradictions* by Rex Warner, copyright, 1938, Alfred A. Knopf, Inc. Reprinted by permission of Alfred A. Knopf, Inc.

J. B. Lippincott Company, for "About the Teeth of Sharks" from *You Read to Me, I'll Read to You* by John Ciardi, copyright, © 1962, Curtis Publishing Company; for "Blue Jay" from *Shoes of the Wind* by Hilda Conkling, copyright, 1922, 1949, Hilda Conkling; for excerpt from "Nursery Rhymes for the Tenderhearted" from *Chimneysmoke* by Christopher Morley, copyright, 1921, 1949, Christopher Morley. Reprinted by permission of J. B. Lippincott Company.

J. B. Lippincott Company and Harold Ober Associates, Inc., for "Cat!" from *Poems for Children* by Eleanor Farjeon, copyright, © 1938, Eleanor Farjeon. Reprinted by permission of J. B. Lippincott Company and Harold Ober Associates, Inc.

The Literary Trustees of Walter de la Mare, for "Five Eyes," "Nicholas Nye," "Quack!" "Tit for Tat," and "Tom's Little Dog" by Walter de la Mare. Reprinted by permission of The Literary Trustees of Walter de la Mare and The Society of Authors as their representative.

Little, Brown & Company and Atlantic Monthly Press, for "A Waltzer in the House" from *Selected Poems 1928-1958* by Stanley Kunitz, copyright, 1951, Stanley Kunitz, originally appeared in *The New Yorker;* for "Seal" from *Boy Blue's Book of Beasts* by William Jay Smith, copyright, © 1956, 1957, William Jay Smith; for "Lion" from *Poems, 1947-1957* by William Jay Smith, copyright, © 1956, William Jay Smith. Reprinted by permission of Little, Brown & Company and Atlantic Monthly Press.

Little, Brown & Company, for "Owls Talking" from *Far and Few* by David McCord, copyright, 1952, David McCord; for "Water Ouzel" from *Odds Without Ends* by David McCord, copyright, 1954, David McCord; for "The Panther" by Ogden Nash, copyright, 1940, the Curtis Publishing Company; "The Kitten" by Ogden Nash, copyright, 1940, Ogden Nash; "The Ostrich" by Ogden Nash, copyright, 1956, Ogden Nash; originally appeared in *The New Yorker;* "The Cow" by Ogden Nash, copyright, 1931, Ogden Nash. Reprinted by permission of Little, Brown & Company.

Albert Mackie, for his poem "Molecatcher." Reprinted by permission of the author.

The Macmillan Company, for "Dark Kingdom" from *Poems* by Elizabeth Coatsworth, copyright, 1957, The Macmillan Company; for "On a Night of Snow" from *Night and the Cat* by Elizabeth Coatsworth, copyright, 1950, The Macmillan Company; for "Sea Gull" from *Summer Green* by Elizabeth Coatsworth, copyright, 1948, The Macmillan Company; for "At the Lion's Cage" from *For Some Stringed Instrument* by Peter Kane Dufault, copyright, 1954, 1955, 1956, 1957, Peter Kane Dufault, first published in *The New Yorker;* for "Something Told the Wild Geese"; from *Branches Green* by Rachel Field, copyright, 1934, The Macmillan Company, renewed, 1962, Arthur S. Pederson; for "Our Lucy" from *The Lordly Hudson* by Paul Goodman, copyright, 1940, 1941, 1947, 1949, 1950, 1951, 1954, 1956, 1957, 1958, 1959, 1960, 1961, 1962, Paul Goodman; for "Dance of Burros" from *Poems from a Cage* by Dilys Laing, copyright, 1952, Alexander Laing; for "The Broncho That Would Not Be Broken" and "The King of Yellow Butterflies" from *Collected Poems* by Vachel Lindsay, copyright, 1917, The Macmillan Company, renewed 1945, Elizabeth C. Lindsay; for "The

Flower-fed Buffaloes" from *Collected Poems* by Vachel Lindsay, copyright, 1913, 1914, 1916, 1917, 1918, 1920, 1923, 1925, The Macmillan Company. Reprinted by permission of The Macmillan Company.

The Macmillan Company and Macmillan & Co. Ltd. London, for "The Blinded Bird" from *Collected Poems* by Thomas Hardy, copyright, 1925, The Macmillan Company; for "The Centaurs" and "The Snare" from *Collected Poems* by James Stephens, copyright, 1915, The Macmillan Company, renewed 1943, James Stephens; for "Little Things" from *Collected Poems* by James Stephens, copyright, 1954, The Macmillan Company. Reprinted by permission of The Macmillan Company and Macmillan & Co. Ltd. London.

The Macmillan Company, Macmillan & Co., Ltd. London, and The Macmillan Company of Canada, Ltd., for "The Bells of Heaven" and "Stupidity Street" from *Collected Poems* by Ralph Hodgson, copyright, 1917, The Macmillan Company, renewed 1945, Ralph Hodgson. Reprinted by permission of The Macmillan Company, Macmillan & Co. Ltd. London, and The Macmillan Company of Canada Limited.

The Macmillan Company and A. D. Peters, for "The Dog from Malta" from *Poems* by Edmund Blunden, first published in 1940. Reprinted by permission of The Macmillan Company and A. D. Peters as Literary Agents for Edmund Blunden.

The Macmillan Company and A. P. Watt & Son, for "The Cat and the Moon" and "To a Squirrel at Kyle-Na-No" from *Collected Poems* by W. B. Yeats, copyright, 1919, The Macmillan Company, renewed 1946, Bertha Georgie Yeats. Reprinted by permission of The Macmillan Company, The Macmillan Company of Canada Limited, A. P. Watt & Son, and Mrs. W. B. Yeats.

Macmillan and Co. Ltd. London, for "The Ponies" from *Fuel* by Wilfrid Gibson. Reprinted by permission of Macmillan and Co. Ltd. London.

McClelland & Stewart Ltd., for "Peacock and Nightingale" by Robert Finch from *The Strength of the Hills;* for "The Bull Calf" by Irving Layton from *A Red Carpet for the Sun.* Reprinted by permission of McClelland & Stewart Ltd.

Winona McClintic, for her poem "Hospitality." Reprinted by permission of the author.

Meredith Press, for "The Herons on Bo Island" from *By Bog and Sea in Donegal* by Elizabeth Shane. Reprinted by permission of Meredith Press.

Mary Britton Miller, for her poems "Cat" and "Foal" from *Menagerie,* published by The Macmillan Company. Reprinted by permission of the author.

Ogden Nash, for his poem "The Hunter" from *Versus,* copyright, 1948, Ogden Nash. Reprinted by permission of the author.

The Nation, for "Chain" by Paul Petrie. Reprinted by permission of *The Nation.*

New Directions, for "To the Snake" from *With Eyes at the Back of Our Heads* by Denise Levertov, © 1958, 1959, Denise Levertov Goodman; for "Poem" from *Selected Poems of William Carlos Williams,* copyright, 1949, William Carlos Williams. Reprinted by permission of New Directions, Publishers.

The New Republic, for "Watching Bird" by Louis O. Coxe. Reprinted by permission of *The New Republic.*

The New Yorker Magazine, Inc., for "Fingers in the Nesting Box" by Robert Graves, © 1958, The New Yorker Magazine, Inc.; for "Denise" by Robert Beverly Hale, © 1958, The New Yorker Magazine, Inc.; for "Fire Island Walking Song" by Eugene F. Kinkead, copyright, © 1957, The New Yorker Magazine, Inc.; for "Hector the Dog" by Kate Barnes, © 1961, The New Yorker Magazine, Inc. Reprinted by permission of The New Yorker Magazine, Inc.

Hugh Noyes, for "The Cure" by Alfred Noyes from *A Letter to Lucian,* published by J. B. Lippincott Company. Reprinted by permission of Hugh Noyes.

Oxford University Press, for "Death of the Cat," "The Fox Rhyme," and

"The Mouse in the Wainscot" from *The Tale of the Monster Horse* by Ian Serraillier; for "The Hare and the Tortoise," "The Hen and the Carp," and "The Squirrel" from *Thomas and the Sparrow* by Ian Serraillier; for "The Giraffe" from *All Day Long* by Geoffrey Dearmer. Reprinted by permission of Oxford University Press.

Pantheon Books, for "Are You a Marsupial?" and "The Hoopee" from *New Feathers for the Old Goose* by John Becker, copyright ©, John Becker; for "Whippoorwill" from *Listen—The Birds* by Mary Britton Miller, copyright © 1961, Pantheon Books, Inc. Reprinted by permission of Pantheon Books, a division of Random House, Inc.

Playboy Press, for "About the Bloath," "Not Me," and "When the Sline Comes to Dine" from *Silverstein's Zoo* by Shelley Silverstein. Reprinted by permission of Playboy Press.

Lawrence Pollinger Ltd., for "A Living" from *The Complete Poems of D. H. Lawrence,* published by The Viking Press, Inc. and William Heinemann Ltd. Reprinted by permission of Lawrence Pollinger Ltd. and the Estate of the Late Mrs. Frieda Lawrence.

Random House, Inc., for "The House Dog's Grave" from *Be Angry at the Sun and Other Poems* by Robinson Jeffers, copyright, 1941; for "Hurt Hawks" copyright, 1928, renewed 1956, Robinson Jeffers, from *The Selected Poetry of Robinson Jeffers.* Reprinted by permission of Random House, Inc.

Richards Press Ltd., for "O What if the Fowler" by Charles Dalmon from *Flower and Leaf.* Reprinted by permission of Richards Press Ltd.

E. V. Rieu and E. P. Dutton & Co., Inc., for "The Happy Hedgehog," "The Lost Cat," "Meditations of a Tortoise," "Night Thoughts of a Tortoise," "Soliloquy of a Tortoise," and "The Unicorn" from *The Flattered Flying Fish and Other Poems* by E. V. Rieu, copyright, © 1962, by E. V. Rieu. Reprinted by permission of the author and E. P. Dutton & Co., Inc.

W. W. E. Ross, for his poems "Fish" and "The Snake Trying." Reprinted by permission of the author.

The Ben Roth Agency Inc., for "Pets" by Daniel Pettiward, ©, PUNCH, London; for "I Had a Hippopotamus" by Patrick Barrington, ©, PUNCH, London; for "The Donkey" by Gertrude Hind, ©, PUNCH, London; for "The Cats" by Jan Struther, ©, PUNCH, London. Reprinted by permission of The Ben Roth Agency, Inc.

The Ryerson Press, for "Exile" by Virna Sheard from *Leaves in the Wind.* Reprinted by permission of The Ryerson Press.

Mrs. Lew Sarett, for "Blacktail Deer," "Four Little Foxes," and "Impasse" from *Covenant With Earth*, by Lew Sarett, edited and copyrighted, 1956, Alma Johnson Sarett, published by University of Florida Press, Gainesville, 1956. Reprinted by permission of Mrs. Lew Sarett.

Charles Scribners' Sons, for "Ducks' Ditty" from *The Wind in the Willows* by Kenneth Grahame; for "The Crayfish" and "The Garden Snail" from *This Various World and Other Poems* by Robert Wallace, copyright, ©, 1956, Robert Wallace, first published in *The New Yorker;* for "Cat and the Weather" from *To Mix With Time* by May Swenson, copyright, ©, 1963, May Swenson; for "Hunting Song," copyright, ©, 1959, Donald Finkel, from *The Clothing's New Emperor and Other Poems* by Donald Finkel. POETS OF TODAY VI. Reprinted by permission of Charles Scribners' Sons.

Martin Secker & Warburg Ltd., for "The Snare" by Patrick MacDonogh from *One Landscape Still.* Reprinted by permission of Martin Secker & Warburg Ltd.

Sidgwick & Jackson Ltd., for excerpt from "Ducks" from *Ducks and Other Poems* by F. W. Harvey. Reprinted by permission of Sidgwick and Jackson Ltd.

Shelley Silverstein, for his poem "The Clam." Reprinted by permission of the author.

Sir Osbert Sitwell, for his poem "The Lament of the Mole-Catcher." Reprinted by permission of the author.

Harrison Smith, for "The Captive Lion," "A Child's Pet," "Jenny Wren," and "Sport" from *The Collected Poems of W. H. Davies,* published by Alfred A. Knopf, Inc. Reprinted by permission of Harrison Smith.

St. Martin's Press Inc. and Macmillan & Co. Ltd. London, for "Au Jardin des Plantes" from *Weep Before God* by John Wain. Reprinted by permission of St. Martin's Press and Macmillan & Co. Ltd. London.

Raymond Souster, for his poems "Dog, Midwinter" and "Squirrel with Jays." Reprinted by permission of the author.

Allan Swallow, Publisher, for "Porcupine" from *Early Rain* by Bert Meyers, copyright, 1960, Bert Meyers; for "April" from *Collected Poems* by Yvor Winters, copyright, 1952, 1960, Yvor Winters. Reprinted by permission of the publisher, Allan Swallow.

Mrs. Helen Thomas, for "The Gallows" by Edward Thomas. Reprinted by permission of Mrs. Helen Thomas.

The Viking Press, Inc., for "Snake" from *Collected Poems* by D. H. Lawrence, copyright, 1929, Jonathan Cape and Harrison Smith, 1956, Frieda Lawrence Ravagli; for "The Hens," "The Rabbit" and "Horse" from *Under the Tree* by Elizabeth Madox Roberts, copyright, 1922, B. W. Huebsch, Inc., 1950, Ivor S. Roberts; for "Nosegay for a Young Goat" from *Blossoming Antlers* by Winifred Welles, copyright, 1933, Winifred Welles. Reprinted by permission of The Viking Press, Inc.

The Viking Press, Inc. and Chatto and Windus Ltd. for "Lone Dog" from *Songs to Save a Soul* by Irene Rutherford McLeod, all rights reserved. Reprinted by permission of The Viking Press, Inc. and Chatto and Windus Ltd.

Vernon Watkins, for his translation of "Cats" by Theodor Storm, published in *Unicorn* magazine. Reprinted by permission of Vernon Watkins.

A. P. Watt & Son, for "The Centipede," "The Chameleon," and "The Oyster" from *The Wherefore and Why* by A. P. Herbert; for "In a Garden" from *Full Enjoyment* by A. P. Herbert. Reprinted by permission of A. P. Watt & Son, Sir Alan Herbert, The Proprietors of Punch, and Methuen & Co. Ltd.

A. P. Watt & Son, for "The Six Badgers" from *Penny Fiddle* by Robert Graves, published by Doubleday & Company, Inc. and Cassell Ltd. Reprinted by permission of A. P. Watt & Son and International Authors N. V.

Wesleyan University Press, for "Cat on Couch" from *Light and Dark* by Barbara Howes, copyright, ©, 1955, Barbara Howes. Reprinted by permission of Wesleyan University Press.

Ann Wolfe, for "The Grey Squirrel" by Humbert Wolfe from *Kensington Gardens.* Reprinted by permission of Ann Wolfe.

Ralph Wotherspoon, for his poem "Our Dumb Friends." Reprinted by permission of the author.

Yale University Press, for "Little City" from *A Beginning* by Robert Horan. Reprinted by permission of Yale University Press.

Avrahm Yarmolinsky, for "Rooster" by Fyodor Belkin, and "Baby Camel" by Vadim Korostylev (translated by Babette Deutsch). Reprinted by permission of Avrahm Yarmolinsky.

Avrahm Yarmolinsky and The Macmillan Company, for "Eagles" by Vasily Bashkin (translated by Babette Deutsch) from *A Treasury of Russian Verse,* copyright, 1949, The Macmillan Company. Reprinted by permission of Avrahm Yarmolinsky and The Macmillan Company.

Contents

Introduction

I once knew a man who had a burning ambition to own a hyena. He wanted to get a baby one, and bring it up with loving care; lead it about on a leash and make it a real pal. "But why a *hyena!*" I asked, and he answered that he felt sorry for them; nobody ever says a kind word for hyenas and they're the most despised of all animals, ". . . and it just isn't *fair!*" He eventually did find out that a properly brought up hyena can be a pleasant outdoor companion, but, alas! he also discovered that, no matter how often washed and tidied, any hyena smells bad. He lived in a city apartment and decided that he'd rather have a lot of human friends than one hyena friend. And it was just as well; a hyena is a wild beast, and should be left that way.

His reason for liking hyenas was peculiar, but understandable. As the ancient saying goes, " 'There's no accounting for tastes,' the old woman said as she kissed the cow." Everyone has his favorite animal, but generally the favorites are the animals we're familiar with: cats, dogs, and horses. I've found upon reading thousands of animal poems that the *poet's* favorite animal is the fox. They're fascinated by the "quick little smarty" who outwits the hunters and boldly steals into the farmer's hen coop. He's the cunning, humorous prankster of the animal world. Poets also like to write about mice, probably because they, too, are bold and amusing. In fact, I suspect that poets like to write about any animal who "puts things over" on the human species. That's all to the good, for we human beings have treated our animal brethren very poorly; we take away their dignity by barring them up in zoos, we use their strength for pulling and carrying, we call it "sport" to hunt them and kill them. And we use them for our amusement, teaching them tricks that are not at all the kind of thing they would be, or should be, doing. Doctor Samuel Johnson once said, "I'd rather see a man on four legs than a dog on two."

You will find that many of the poems in this collection are concerned with man's cruelty to animals; with poor blind ponies who spend their whole lives in the darkness of a mine; with innocent, wounded animals caught all night long in traps, or, as Ralph Hodgson wrote:

> I saw with open eyes
> Singing birds sweet
> Sold in the shops
> For the people to eat,
> Sold in the shops of
> Stupidity Street.

Cruelty to animals is the greatest sin; such cruelty in a man shows that he has grown up with no reverence for life itself—for the miracle of any living thing. People are sometimes cruel from plain thick stupidity, and sometimes—which is even worse—because it makes them feel superior to mistreat or kill an innocent animal. There's some of this cruelty in anyone who hunts just for the sport of it, who hunts not because he is hungry or needs warm skins but for the sport of killing. Oscar Wilde said of hunting: "The English country gentleman galloping after a fox—the unspeakable in full pursuit of the uneatable."

There should be a few surprises—a few shocks—in every collection of poetry. In this one you'll find "Night Song of the Fish" by the German poet Christian Morgenstern (page 67). This is a poem without any words. Ridiculous, but it is. And I believe you'll understand it at a glance. However, when you come to E. E. Cummings' poem "r-p-o-p-h-e-s-s-a-g-r" (page 225) you'll probably think that the man who set the type for this book suddenly went out of his mind. But, no, there *is* a grasshopper there. If you've ever watched a grasshopper, you'll have noticed that, before he leaps, he's a tidy, well-put-together insect—a grasshopper; but when he does leap his wings and legs go every-which-way. By rearranging the letters in "grasshopper" the poet gives a feeling of how the insect's appearance changes in his leap, and by using occasional capital letters among the small letters, he even gives something of how the grasshopper sounds. If you puzzle it out, the poem reads something like: "as we look . . . gathering up now to leap . . . leaps! . . . arriving to become, rearrangingly, grasshopper." Don't, however, try to read this poem out loud.

The only other poems that might seem difficult are those in Scots dialect, but they're easy once you get the hang of it, and the footnotes, defining the more difficult Scottish words, should help. The footnotes for one of the poems—Albert D. Mackie's "Molecatcher" (page 40)—are longer than the poem itself, but it is surprising how much of the poem you can understand right off, without knowing exactly what most of the words mean. Try it. The poems by Don Marquis have no capital letters, which is puzzling unless you know that they were written by his friend archy, the cockroach, on Mr. Marquis' typewriter. As everybody knows, cockroaches can't make capital letters when they use a typewriter.

My own favorite nature poets are W. H. Davies, James Stephens, Walter de la Mare, and, most of all, John Clare, who was *the* nature poet. Clare, who died a hundred years ago, was the son of a poor English farmer. He was a strange child who spent his days roaming the fields; he was once found many miles away from his home, and explained that he had been searching for the horizon. He was uneducated, and although a great poet, was a perfectly awful speller and knew almost nothing about punctuation (which may make some of you feel better). His poems were published during his lifetime, but he never made enough money from them to provide a living, and the farmers with whom he grew up would never hire such an odd fellow, even as a laborer. Money problems unsettled his mind, and he spent the last twenty-five years of his life in an asylum where, incidentally, he wrote many of his loveliest poems. If you like nature poetry, get a book of his from your library.

I remember once asking a friend, returned from a long walk, if he'd seen anything interesting. "Oh, nothing much," he replied, "but I met some nice dogs." *That* made the walk worthwhile. It's such a delight, such a present, really, to be in the country and unexpectedly come upon a field of animals—to stand in wonder before the clean, matted beauty of a velvet-muzzled calf; to watch a ridiculously lovable lamb; to see a high-legged colt showing such an obvious joy of life. An even greater gift from nature is to come upon a wild animal in the woods or fields; to see, as he *really* is, a woodchuck, a deer, a rabbit. There seems almost to be a mutual moment of communication before the animal leaps or scurries off.

One of the great things a poet can do, which no writer of prose really can, is to celebrate the animals, to praise their grace, their beauty, and the honesty of their instincts. As Walter de la Mare said, "Animals glorify the earth." And so do poets.

WILLIAM COLE

Small Animals of the Woods and Fields

Blairsville Junior High School
Blairsville, Pennsylvania

Hunting Song

The fox came lolloping, lolloping,
Lolloping. His tongue hung out
And his ears were high.
He was like death at the end of a string
When he came to the hollow
Log. Ran in one side
And out of the other. O
He was sly.

The hounds came tumbling, tumbling,
Tumbling. Their heads were low
And their eyes were red.
The sound of their breath was louder than death
When they came to the hollow
Log. They held at one end
But a bitch found the scent. O
They were mad.

The hunter came galloping, galloping,
Galloping. All damp was his mare
From her hooves to her mane.
His coat and his mouth were redder than death
When he came to the hollow

Blairsville Junior High School
Blairsville, Pennsylvania

Log. He took in the rein
And over he went. O
He was fine.

The log, he just lay there, alone in
The clearing. No fox nor hound
Nor mounted man
Saw his black round eyes in their perfect disguise
(As the ends of a hollow
Log). He watched death go through him,
Around him and over him. O
He was wise.

DONALD FINKEL

Mouses's Nest

I found a ball of grass among the hay
And progged it as I passed and went away;
And when I looked I fancied something stirred,
And turned again and hoped to catch the bird—
When out an old mouse bolted in the wheats
With all her young ones hanging at her teats;
She looked so odd and so grotesque to me,
I ran and wondered what the thing could be,
And pushed the knapweed bunches where I stood;
Then the mouse hurried from the craking* brood.
The young ones squeaked, and as I went away
She found her nest again among the hay.
The water o'er the pebbles scarce could run
And broad old cesspools glittered in the sun.

JOHN CLARE

* craking: crying out

The Snare

I hear a sudden cry of pain!
There is a rabbit in a snare;
Now I hear the cry again,
But I cannot tell from where.

But I cannot tell from where.
He is calling out for aid!
Crying on the frightened air,
Making everything afraid!

Making everything afraid!
Wrinkling up his little face!
As he cries again for aid;
—And I cannot find the place!

And I cannot find the place
Where his paw is in the snare!
Little One! Oh, Little One!
I am searching everywhere!

JAMES STEPHENS

The Bat

Airy-mouse, hairy mouse,
Keen-eared contrary mouse,
Come from your cavern—a star's in the sky!
Fluttering, flittering,
Eerily chittering,
Swoop on your quarry, the dusk-haunting fly.

Airy-mouse, wary mouse,
Witch-bird or fairy-mouse
Soft through the shadow the dawn-glimmer steals;
Night's your carousing-time,
Day brings your drowsing-time;
Hence to your hollow and hang by your heels!

ARTHUR GUITERMAN

The Lament of the Mole-Catcher

An old, sad man who catches moles
Went lonely down the lane—
All lily-green were the lanes and knolls
But sorrow numbed his brain.
He paid no heed to flower or weed
And went his lonely way.
No note he heard from any bird
That sang that sad spring day.

"I trapp'd the moles for forty years,
Who could not see the sky,
I reckoned not blind blood or tears,
And the Lord has seen them die.
For forty years I've sought to slay
The small, the dumb, the blind,
And now the Lord has made me pay,
And I am like their kind.
I cannot see or lane or hill,
Or flower or bird or moon;
Lest life shall lay me lower still,
O Lord—come take it soon."

OSBERT SITWELL

The Rabbit

When they said the time to hide was mine,
I hid back under a thick grape vine.

And while I was still for the time to pass,
A little gray thing came out of the grass.

He hopped his way through the melon bed
And sat down close by a cabbage head.

He sat down close where I could see,
And his big still eyes looked hard at me,

His big eyes bursting out of the rim,
And I looked back very hard at him.

ELIZABETH MADOX ROBERTS

Squirrel with Jays

Bird cries, bird-threshings
from the poplar tree:
                    it's that squirrel again!
He's found the two jays
that set up light housekeeping
two days ago:
                    up the trunk he goes
almost to the nest,
but the jays are ready
and dive-bomb him down
this tree to the other

(feint of feather
flutter-fast)
and after him, arrowing
right to the ground,

but both sides wary
respectful of the other,
the squirrel I think now
playing more than anything,
content to let it go
at least for today
but *tomorrow* very much
in his fur-scrapped head
as he hugs the tree bark
and waits
        waits
                waits

RAYMOND SOUSTER

Of Foxes

The gray fox for the mountains—
   The gray fox walks alone
In scorn of any comrade
   Saye waterfall and stone.
A sparrow for his dinner,
   A cavern for his bed,
The mist-hung world below him,
   A thin moon overhead;
Long hours for meditation
   On mating time and spring,
On hidden oblique pathways
   Or how the planets swing.

Austerity confirms him
  A proper denizen
    For the fastness of the mountains,
      The solitude of mountains.
        And, keeping to the mountains,
  He traffics not with men.

The red fox for the lowlands—
  The red fox has a need
For measuring his cunning,
  For matching speed with speed.
He knows the taste of ducklings
  Made fat by farmers' corn;
He savors the elation
  Of huntsman, hounds and horn.
O splendid hour of testing:
  Outguessing every guess,
Outwitting duller creatures
  With delicate finesse!
And when the chase is ended
  He flaunts his brush again,
    A bright torch through the lowlands
      To fire the stolid lowlands,
        A challenge to the lowlands
For the "view halloo" of men.

B. Y. WILLIAMS

A Waltzer in the House

A sweet, a delicate white mouse,
A little blossom of a beast,
Is waltzing in the house
Among the crackers and the yeast.

O the swaying of his legs!
O the bobbing of his head!
The lady, beautiful and kind,
The blue-eyed mistress, lately wed,
Has almost laughed away her wits
To see the pretty mouse that sits
On his tiny pink behind
And swaying, bobbing, begs.

She feeds him tarts and curds,
Seed packaged for the birds,
And figs, and nuts, and cheese;
Polite as Pompadour to please
The dainty waltzer of her house,
The sweet, the delicate, the innocent white mouse.

As in a dream, as in a trance,
She loves his rhythmic elegance,
She laughs to see his bobbing dance.

STANLEY KUNITZ

Chipmunks

You nest in roof-tops where your scratching feet
Make sounds at night as small as rain or sleet.

At sky-high window sills on crumbs you feed.
To nibble blossoms richly gone to seed,

You stretch out over a canyon's dizzy brink.
Up slippery trees you gallop gay and quick.

Though striped with marks like eyebrows white and black
It's hard to see you sitting in your chink

Of the meadow's wall, saying your soft "chuck-chuck,"
With eyes like beads of tar that never blink.

You flirt your downy tail, then do your trick
Of turning into the stripes of sun on rock.

MARNIE POMEROY

The Gallows

There was a weasel lived in the sun
With all his family,
Till a keeper shot him with his gun
And hung him up on a tree,
Where he swings in the wind and rain,
In the sun and in the snow,
Without pleasure, without pain,
On the dead oak tree bough.

There was a crow who was no sleeper,
But a thief and a murderer
Till a very late hour; and this keeper
Made him one of the things that were,
To hang and flap in rain and wind
In the sun and in the snow.
There are no more sins to be sinned
On the dead oak tree bough.

There was a magpie, too,
Had a long tongue and a long tail;
He could both talk and do—
But what did that avail?
He, too, flaps in the wind and rain
Alongside weasel and crow,

Without pleasure, without pain,
On the dead oak tree bough.

And many other beasts
And birds, skin, bone, and feather,
Have been taken from their feasts
And hung up there together.
To swing and have endless leisure
In the sun and in the snow,
Without pain, without pleasure,
On the dead oak tree bough.

EDWARD THOMAS

The Rabbit

Hearing the hawk squeal in the high sky
I and the rabbit trembled.
Only the dark small rabbits newly kittled in their neatly dissembled
Hollowed nest in the thicket thatched with straw
Did not respect his cry.
At least, not that I saw.

But I have said to the rabbit with rage and a hundred times, "Hop!
Streak it for the bushes! Why do you sit so still?
You are bigger than a house, I tell you, you are bigger than a hill, you are a beacon for airplanes!
O indiscreet!
And the hawk and all my friends are out to kill.
Get under cover!" But the rabbit never stirred; she never will.

And I shall see again and again the large eye blaze
With death, and gently glaze;
The leap into the air I shall see again and again, and the kicking feet;
And the sudden quiet everlasting, and the blade of grass green in the strange mouth of the interrupted grazer.

EDNA ST. VINCENT MILLAY

The Happy Hedgehog

The happiness of hedgehogs
Lies in complete repose.
They spend the months of winter
In a long delicious doze;
And if they note the time at all
They think "How fast it goes!"

E. V. RIEU

The Fox Rhyme

Aunt was on the garden seat
Enjoying a wee nap and
Along came a fox! teeth
Closed with a snap and
He's running to the woods with her
A-dangle and a-flap and—
Run, uncle, run
And see what has happened!

IAN SERRAILLIER

The Squirrel

Among the fox-red fallen leaves I surprised him. Snap
up the chestnut bole he leapt,
the brown leaper, clawing up-swept:
turned on the first bough and scolded me roundly.
That's right, load me with reviling,
spit at me, swear horrible, shame me if you can.
But scared of my smiling
off and up he scurries. Now Jack's up the beanstalk
among the dizzy giants. He skips
along the highest branches, along
tree-fingers slender as string,
fur tail following, to the very tips:
then leaps the aisle—
O fear he fall
a hundred times his little length!
He's over! clings, swings on a spray,
then lightly, the ghost of a mouse, against the sky traces
for me his runway of rare wonder, races
helter-skelter without pause or break
(I think of the snail—how long would he take?)
on and onward, not done yet—
his errand? some nut-plunder, you bet.
Oh he's gone!
I peer and search and strain for him, but he's gone.
I wait and watch at the giants' feet, among
the fox-red fallen leaves. One drop
of rain lands with a smart tap
on the drum, on parchment leaf. I wait
and wait and shiver and forget . . .

A fancy: suppose these trees, so ancient, so
venerable, so rock-rooted, suddenly

heaved up their huge elephantine hooves
(O the leaves, how they'd splutter and splash
like a waterfall, a red waterfall)—suppose
they trudged away!
What would the squirrel say?

IAN SERRAILLIER

Rats!

Rats!
They fought the dogs and killed the cats,
And bit the babies in the cradles,
And ate the cheeses out of the vats,
And licked the soup from the cook's own ladles
Split open the kegs of salted sprats,
Made nests inside men's Sunday hats,
And even spoiled the women's chats,
By drowning their speaking
With shrieking and squeaking
In fifty different sharps and flats.

ROBERT BROWNING
(from *The Pied Piper of Hamelin*)

Lèse Majesté

The Lion ramps around the cage,
The Lady smiles to see him rage.
The little Mouse outside the bars
Looks on and laughs. "Well, bless my stars!"
Quoth he, "to think they call that thing
The *King of Beasts!* If *he's* a King,
Who cannot make the Lady wince,
What must *I* be? When, not long since,
Inside the cage I chanced to slip,
You should have seen that Lady skip
Upon the Lion's back. 'Help! Murder!
A Mouse!' she screamed; you should have heard her!
And then with brooms the keepers came
And drove me out (but, all the same,
I got the crumb that I was after).
A King indeed! Excuse my laughter!"

OLIVER HERFORD

Ground Hog Day

In February when few gusty flakes
Above the frozen sheets of snow still hover,
Out of his hole the sleepy ground hog breaks
To peek around and see if winter's over.

Now if he find his shadow, back he shies
To nap while deeper drifts the wind shall bring;
But if no shadow shows beneath dark skies
He waddles through the ditch to look for spring.

MARNIE POMEROY

The Six Badgers

As I was a-hoeing, a-hoeing my lands
Six badgers came up with white wands in their hands
They made a ring around me and, bowing, they said:
"Hurry home, Farmer George, for the table is spread!
There's pie in the oven, there's beef on the plate:
Hurry home, Farmer George, if you would not be late!"
So homeward I went, but could not understand
Why six fine dog-badgers with white wands in hand
Should seek me out hoeing and bow in a ring,
And all to inform me so common a thing!

ROBERT GRAVES

The Vixen

Among the taller wood with ivy hung,
The old fox plays and dances round her young.
She snuffs and barks if any passes by
And swings her tail and turns prepared to fly.
The horseman hurries by, she bolts to see,
And turns agen, from danger never free.
If any stands she runs among the poles*
And barks and snaps and drives them in the holes.
The shepherd sees them and the boy goes by
And gets a stick and progs the hole to try.
They get all still and lie in safety sure,
And out again when everything's secure,
And start and snap at blackbirds bouncing by
To fight and catch the great white butterfly.

JOHN CLARE

* poles: cubs

To Three Small Rabbits in a Burrow

The garden is a gilded cage
blazing in beauty,
The garden is your heritage,
To eat it, rabbit duty.

Nibble, nibble a way out
in an autumn hour.
Is there any other way
to enjoy a flower?

MARY KENNEDY

The Opossum

At dusk I met you first where the dirt road bends.
Your litter of six, too big to ride in your pouch,
Clung to your heavy tail. At my approach
You hauled them away, running on all four hands.

Next day, surprised, you were scavenging by the dump.
No time to play dead possum. Too small to fight,
You glared at me silent and stiff and apt to bite.
I felt your scaly tail but kept ready to jump.

Like a magnified rat's it was. I studied your face
Dead-white, tipped with that india-rubber nose.
I looked from your black paper ears to your fingers in rows
Till you hissed and fumbled along on your garbage chase.

MARNIE POMEROY

Four Little Foxes

Speak gently, Spring, and make no sudden sound;
For, in my windy valley, yesterday I found
New-born foxes squirming on the ground—
Speak gently.

Walk softly, March, forbear the bitter blow;
Her feet within a trap, her blood upon the snow,
The four little foxes saw their mother go—
Walk softly.

Go lightly, Spring, oh, give them no alarm;
When I covered them with boughs to shelter them from harm,
The thin blue foxes suckled at my arm—
Go lightly.

Step softly, March, with your rampant hurricane;
Nuzzling one another, and whimpering with pain,
The new little foxes are shivering in the rain—
Step softly.

LEW SARETT

Squirrel in Sunshine

Drawn from his refuge in some lonely elm
That age or injury has hollow'd deep,
Where, on his bed of wool and matted leaves
He has outslept the winter, ventures forth
To frisk awhile, the bask in the warm sun,
The squirrel, flippant, pert, and full of play:

He sees me, and at once, swift as a bird
Ascends the neighbouring beech; there whisks his brush,
And perks his ears, and stamps, and cries aloud
With all the prettiness of feign'd alarm
And anger insignificantly fierce.

WILLIAM COWPER

To a Mouse

ON TURNING HER UP IN HER NEST WITH
THE PLOUGH, NOVEMBER, 1785

Wee, sleekit, cowrin, tim'rous beastie,
O, what a panic's in thy breastie!
Thou need na start awa sae hasty,
Wi' bickering brattle*!
I wad be laith to rin an' chase thee,
Wi' murd'ring pattle*!

I'm truly sorry Man's dominion
Has broken Nature's social union,
An' justifies that ill opinion
Which makes thee startle
At me, thy poor, earth-born companion,
An' fellow-mortal!

I doubt na, whyles, but thou may thieve
What then? poor beastie, thou maun live!
A daimen* icker* in a thrave*
'S a sma' request.
I'll get a blessin wi' the lave,
And never miss't!

Thy wee bit housie, too, in ruin!
Its silly wa's the win's are strewin!

* brattle: scamper
* pattle: plough-staff
* daimen: odd
* icker: ear of corn
* thrave: twenty-four sheaves

An' naethingv, now, to big* a new ane,
O' foggage* green!
An' bleak December's winds ensuin,
Baith snell* and keen!

Thou saw the fields laid bare an' waste,
An' weary Winter comin fast,
An' cozie here, beneath the blast,
Thou thought to dwell,
Till crash! the cruel coulter past
Out thro' thy cell.

That wee bit heap o' leaves an' stibble,
Has cost thee mony a weary nibble!
Now thou's turned out, for a' thy trouble,
But* house or hald*,
To thole* the Winter's sleety dribble,
An' cranreuch* cauld!

But, Mousie, thou are no thy lane*,
In proving foresight may be vain:
The best-laid schemes o' Mice an' Men,
Gang aft a-gley*,
An' lea'e us nought but grief and pain,
For promised joy.

Still thou art blest, compared wi' me!
The present only toucheth thee;
But, Och! I backward cast my e'e,
On prospects drear!
An' forward, tho' I canna see,
I guess an' fear!

ROBERT BURNS

* big: build
* foggage: coarse grass
* snell: biting
* but: without
* hald: holding, land
* thole: endure
* cranreuch: hoar-frost
* lane: by thyself
* a-gley: askew

Young Reynard

I

Gracefullest leaper, the dappled fox-cub
Curves over brambles with berries and buds,
Light as a bubble that flies from the tub,
Whisked by the laundry-wife out of her suds.
Wavy he comes, woolly, all at his ease,
Elegant, fashioned to foot with the deuce;
Nature's own prince of the dance: then he sees
Me, and retires as if making excuse.

II

Never closed minuet courtlier! Soon
Cub-hunting troops were abroad, and a yelp
Told of sure scent: ere the stroke upon noon
Reynard the younger lay far beyond help.
Wild, my poor friend, has the fate to be chased;
Civil will conquer: were 'tother 'twere worse;
Fair, by the flushed early morning embraced,
Haply you live a day longer in verse.

GEORGE MEREDITH

White Season

In the winter the rabbits match their pelts to the earth.
With ears laid back, they go
Blown through the silver hollow, the silver thicket,
Like puffs of snow.

FRANCES M. FROST

The Grey Squirrel

Like a small grey
coffee-pot,
sits the squirrel.
He is not

all he should be,
kills by dozens
trees, and eats
his red-brown cousins.

The keeper on the
other hand
, who shot him, is
a Christian, and

loves his enemies,
which shows
the squirrel was not
one of those.

HUMBERT WOLFE

The Masked Shrew

. . . The Masked Shrew . . . approximately one year of fast-paced gluttonous life. Life Magazine.

A penny is heavier than the shrew,
dim-eyed and weaker than a worm
this smallest mammal, cannoned by a sudden noise,
lies down and dies.

No furnaced gluttons fiercer than the shrew
devouring daily with relentless appetite
four times her inchling body's weight.
More extravagant than the hummingbird's the shrew's
heart beats per minute twice four hundred times.
If foodless for six hours she is dead.
The helpless, hungry, nervous shrew
lives for a year of hurly-burly
and dies intolerably early.

ISABELLA GARDNER

Molecatcher

Strampin'* the bent*, like the Angel o' Daith,
The mowdie-man* staves by;
Alang his pad the mowdie-worps*
Like sma' Assyrians lie.

And where the Angel o' Daith has been,
Yirked* oot o' their yirdy* hames,
Lie Sennacherib's blasted hosts
Wi' guts dung* oot o' wames*.

Sma' black tramorts* wi' gruntles* grey,
Sma' weak weemin's han's,
Sma' bead-een that wid touch ilk hert
Binnae* the mowdie-man's.

ALBERT D. MACKIE

* strampin : tramping
* bent: open field
* mowdie-man: molecatcher
* mowdie-worps: moles
* yirked: jerked
* yirdy: earthy
* dung: knocked
* wames: bellies, stomachs
* tramorts: corpses
* gruntles: snouts
* binnae: except

Concrete Trap

The fox at midnight in the city square
knows there's a way, but knows not which it is,
a path that leads to fields and woods and lair,
leaves underfoot, earth and the stirring air.
Bewildered stands the fox, too many streets
lead off too many ways, yet there is one
leads to the woods and to tomorrow's sun.
Under street lamps, between the straight house walls,
hard, geometric, baffling nose and eyes,
escape is there for him to recognize.
Bewildered stands the fox, questing the way,
and in the yards the dogs begin to bay.

ELIZABETH COATSWORTH

The Mouse

I heard a mouse
Bitterly complaining
In a crack of moonlight
Aslant on the floor—

"Little I ask
And that little is not granted.
There are few crumbs
In this world any more.

"The bread-box is tin
And I cannot get in.

"The jam's in a jar
My teeth cannot mar.

"The cheese sits by itself
On the pantry shelf—

"All night I run
Searching and seeking,
All night I run
About on the floor,

"Moonlight is there
And a bare place for dancing,
But no little feast
Is spread any more."

ELIZABETH COATSWORTH

The Field Mouse

When the moon shines o'er the corn
And the beetle drones his horn,
And the flittermice swift fly,
And the nightjars swooping cry,
And the young hares run and leap,
We waken from our sleep.

And we climb with tiny feet
And we munch the green corn sweet
With startled eyes for fear
The white owl should fly near,
Or long slim weasel spring
Upon us where we swing.

We do not hurt at all;
Is there not room for all
Within the happy world?

All day we lie close curled
In drowsy sleep, nor rise
Till through the dusky skies
The moon shines o'er the corn
And the beetle drones his horn.

WILLIAM SHARP

To a Squirrel at Kyle-Na-No

Come play with me;
Why should you run
Through the shaking tree
As though I'd a gun
To strike you dead?
When all I would do
Is to scratch your head
And let you go.

WILLIAM BUTLER YEATS

A Dead Mole

Strong-shouldered mole,
That so much lived below the ground,
Dug, fought and loved, hunted and fed,
For you to raise a mound
Was as for us to make a hole;
What wonder now that being dead
Your body lies here stout and square
Buried within the blue vault of the air?

ANDREW YOUNG

Tatterdemalion

A small and pompous alderman
Of a rusty Fox
Has just awakened from a rusty sleep.
He yawns and blinks.
More ticks than tocks
Are characteristic of his thinking,
But his legend mocks
Us in his person.

Is this pitiful little sphinx
The wily rogue who led
The headlong horses
On a merry romp,
Snickering up his mud-soiled sleeve
At their fruitless Puddapomp! Puddapomp!
And the frenzied baying
Of the cluckheaded hounds?

PEGGY BENNETT

The Mouse in the Wainscot

Hush, Suzanne!
Don't lift your cup.
That breath you heard
Is a mouse getting up.

As the mist that steams
From your milk as you sup,
So soft is the sound
Of a mouse getting up.

There! did you hear
His feet pitter-patter,
Lighter than tipping
Of beads on a platter,

And then like a shower
On the window pane
The little feet scampering
Back again?

O falling of feather!
O drift of a leaf!
The mouse in the wainscot
Is dropping asleep.

IAN SERRAILLIER

The Bat

By day the bat is cousin to the mouse.
He likes the attic of an aging house.

His fingers make a hat about his head.
His pulse beat is so slow we think him dead.

He loops in crazy figures half the night
Among the trees that face the corner light.

But when he brushes up against a screen,
We are afraid of what our eyes have seen:

For something is amiss or out of place
When mice with wings can wear a human face.

THEODORE ROETHKE

from *Meeting*

Over the grass a hedgehog came
Questing the air for scents of food
And the cracked twig of danger.
He shuffled near in the gloom. Then stopped.
He was aware of me. I went up,
Bent low to look at him, and saw
His coat of lances pointing to my hand.
What could I do
To show I was no enemy?
I turned him over, inspected his small clenched paws,
His eyes expressionless as glass,
And did not know how I could speak,
By tongue or touch the language of a friend.

CLIFFORD DYMENT

from *Annus Mirabilis*

So have I seen some fearful hare maintain
   A course till tired before the dog she lay;
Who, stretched behind her, pants upon the plain,
   Past pow'r to kill as she to get away.

With his lolled tongue he faintly licks his prey,
   His warm breath blows her flix* up as she lies;
She, trembling, creeps upon the ground away,
   And looks back to him with beseeching eyes.

JOHN DRYDEN

* flix: downy fur

Sport

Hunters, hunters,
Follow the Chase.
I saw the Fox's eyes,
Not in his face
But on it, big with fright—
Haste, hunters, haste!

Say, hunters, say
Is it a noble sport?
As rats that bite
Babies in cradles, so,
Such rats and men
Take their delight.

W. H. DAVIES

Epitaph on a Hare

Here lies, whom hound did ne'er pursue,
   Nor swifter greyhound follow,
Whose foot ne'er tainted morning dew,
   Nor ear heard huntsman's halloo.

Old Tiney, surliest of his kind,
   Who, nursed with tender care,
And to domestic bounds confined,
   Was still a wild Jack-hare.

Though duly from my hand he took
   His pittance every night,

He did it with a jealous look
   And, when he could, would bite.

His diet was of wheaten bread,
   And milk, and oats, and straw;
Thistles, or lettuces instead,
   With sand to scour his maw.

On twigs of hawthorn he regaled,
   On pippins' russet peel,
And when his juicy salads failed,
   Sliced carrot pleased him well.

A Turkey carpet was his lawn,
   Whereon he loved to bound,
To skip and gambol like a fawn,
   And swing his rump around.

His frisking was at evening hours,
   For then he lost his fear,
But most before approaching showers
   Or when a storm drew near.

Eight years and five round-rolling moons
He thus saw steal away,
Dozing out all his idle noons,
And every night at play.

I kept him for his humour's sake,
For he would oft beguile
My heart of thoughts that made it ache,
And force me to a smile.

But now beneath his walnut shade
He finds his long last home,
And waits, in snug concealment laid,
Till gentler puss shall come.

He, still more aged, feels the shocks,
From which no care can save,
And, partner once of Tiney's box,
Must soon partake his grave.

WILLIAM COWPER

January

The fox drags its wounded belly
Over the snow, the crimson seeds
Of blood burst with a mild explosion,
Soft as excrement, bold as roses.

Over the snow that feels no pity,
Whose white hands can give no healing,
The fox drags its wounded belly.

R. S. THOMAS

Badger

When midnight comes a host of boys and men
Go out and track the badger to his den,
And put a sack within the hole, and lie
Till the old grunting badger passes by.
He comes and hears—they let the strongest loose.
The old fox hears the noise and drops the goose.
The poacher shoots and hurries from the cry,
And the old hare half wounded buzzes by.
They get a forked stick to bear him down
And clap the dogs and take him to the town,
And bait him all the day with many dogs,
And laugh and shout and fright the scampering hogs.
He runs along and bites at all he meets:
They shout and hollo down the noisy streets.

He turns about to face the loud uproar
And drives the rebels to their very door.
The frequent stone is hurled where'er they go;
When badgers fight, then every one's a foe.
The dogs are clapt and urged to join the fray;
The badger turns and drives them all away.
Though scarcely half as big, demure and small,
He fights with dogs for hours and beats them all.
The heavy mastiff, savage in the fray,
Lies down and licks his feet and turns away.
The bulldog knows his match and waxes cold,
The badger grins and never leaves his hold.
He drives the crowd and follows at their heels
And bites them through—the drunkard swears and reels.

The frightened women take the boys away,
The blackguard laughs and hurries on the fray.

He tries to reach the woods, an awkward race,
But sticks and cudgels quickly stop the chase.
He turns agen and drives the noisy crowd
And beats the many dogs in noises loud.
He drives away and beats them every one,
And then they loose them all and set them on.
He falls as dead and kicked by boys and men,
Then starts and grins and drives the crowd agen;
Till kicked and torn and beaten out he lies
And leaves his hold and cackles, groans, and dies.

JOHN CLARE

Hospitality

Little beast behind the rafter,
Is it raisins you are after?
Have a cornflake;
Carve the cupcake.
Will you share a dish of tay?
Ought I offer you canned pease?
"-------more cheese!-------"

Little creature of the alley,
Are you hungry, are you really?
Gnaw on cold cuts;
Chaw Brazil nuts.
Can you try my consommé?
Taste these lights and livers, please.
"-------More Cheese!-------"

Little monster in the night,
In rye biscuits you may bite.

Munch this mustard;
Crunch some custard.
Could you care for curds and whey,
Spicy ham or mess of pottage,
Heated Spam or pot of message,
Shrimp, crab, lobster from the seas?
"-------MORE CHEESE!-------"

WINONA McCLINTIC

The Bat

Lightless, unholy, eldritch* thing,
Whose murky and erratic wing
Swoops so sickeningly, and whose
Aspect to the female Muse
Is a demon's, made of stuff
Like tattered, sooty waterproof,
Looking dirty, clammy, cold.

Wicked, poisonous, and old;
I have maligned thee! . . . for the Cat
Lately caught a little bat,
Seized it softly, bore it in.
On the carpet, dark as sin
In the lamplight, painfully
It limped about, and could not fly.

Even fear must yield to love,
And pity make the depths to move.
Though sick with horror, I must stoop,
Grasp it gently, take it up,
And carry it, and place it where
It could resume the twilight air.

* eldritch: eerie

Strange revelation! warm as milk,
Clean as a flower, smooth as silk!
O what a piteous face it appears,
What great fine thin translucent ears
What chestnut down and crapy wings,
Finer than any lady's things—
And O a little one that clings!

Warm, clean, and lovely, though not fair,
And burdened with a mother's care;
Go hunt the hurtful fly, and bear
My Blessing to your kind in air.

RUTH PITTER

The Hunt

The dog fox rolls on his lolling tongue
The frosty grape of the morning.
He points his nose to the scent of day,
He slits his eyes to the yellow sun,
He feels in his haunch a rising thunder
And his lifted ear takes warning:
The horn blows true,
The hounds break through,
The hunter spreads,
The huntsman rides,
And the red-tailed fox goes under.

The dog fox breaks to a hidden hole
And deep in the fern goes under.
He stiffens haunch and poises pads,
He gulps his spittle and drops his tail,
He downs his ears to the gathering thunder,

Crouching as they go over:
    Blowing horn,
    Baying hound,
    Shuddering hoof
    Shaking ground,
And the red-tailed fox stays under.

Heavy the huntsman will fall to bed
And heavily snore till morning.
The hunter will drowse and shake the stall
With a heavy hoof and hang his head.
The hound will whimper, and done with yawning,
Sleep as the moon goes under,
    And deep in the shade
    Of night will creep
    The fox to his feast
    On the feathered roost
And dine till the sun is dawning.

LOUIS KENT

Dark Kingdom

Mice are the citizens of a dark kingdom,
they live between the walls,
they know where misers hide their bags of gold
blocking their secret halls.

Their children lie in nests soft with the ribbons
of shredded love letters and parchment deeds,
and play with old lost rings and dusty jewels
and scattered beads.

ELIZABETH COATSWORTH

Little Things

Little things that run and quail
And die in silence and despair;

Little things that fight and fail
And fall on earth and sea and air;

All trapped and frightened little things,
The mouse, the coney, hear our prayer

As we forgive those done to us,
The lamb, the linnet, and the hare,

Forgive us all our trespasses,
Little creatures everywhere.

JAMES STEPHENS

The Snare

He stoops above the clumsy snare
To take the night's yet living loot,
And the wild creature kicking there
Beside the thorn-tree's tunnelled root,
Flings up red soil into his eyes—
And suddenly the April skies
Are loud with pain of man and brute,
Until he lifts a clabbered boot
And stamps red life into the sod,
And silence takes the fields again—
The old deceptive peace of God!

PATRICK MacDONOGH

The Dormouse

The dormouse chews a hole
The size of himself
And gets into it for the winter.
He lies on his side
With his paws furled
Like the tips of ferns in spring.

If you take a dormouse out of his nest
Before he is awake
He feels cool and heavy.
His hole looks vacant
And repeats his shape after him.

The best thing to do is put him back again.

PATI HILL

Fire Island Walking Song

(Sung, at the top of his voice, by my six-year-old son, while dancing along the beach almost, but not quite, out of the reach of the waves.)

I know a large dune rat whose first name is Joe
And he skips beneath the boardwalk medium slow
Out to the edge where the daylight glisters
And he hasn't any brothers and he hasn't any sisters
And he hasn't any uncles and he hasn't any aunts
And he hasn't any Sunday-go-to-meeting pants.

Oh, he lives all alone in the big tall grassages
And through the brush piles he has secret passages.

He dines on moonbeams and washed-up scobbles
And he never has the toothache or the collywobbles.
He comes out at night and he dances by the sea
And he's a pretty nice dune rat, if you're asking me.

EUGENE F. KINKEAD

Porcupine

A little Saint
Sebastian
(body of barbs
that hardly hurt)
and like a Saint
misunderstood,
when he appears
he scares the wood.

We love to catch
an animal;
then, petting it,
insist the beast
should lick our hand.
But porcupines:
they're very mean
to have such spines.

BERT MEYERS

Under the Water and on the Shore

Over the Green Sands

Leaning on the unpainted rail
We gazed into a fathom of water so clear
We were engulfed,
  And saw a darkness moving

Through the bottle green,
  A shadow creeping
Over the pale floor of tinted sand,
Coarse hair coiling and weaving—

Yet not a hair was displaced.
It was an enormous school of miniature
  Fish who laced
The quiet flood with their immaculate coiffure.

Quivering up in precise formations,
The mannered swarm, cutting and hitching,
Threaded the water with live needles
  Which left no stitching.

We dropped our pebbles. The tiny darts
  Swerved wild.
Fluttering, badly mussed,
They hesitated for an instant.

  Then away they streaked,
Beside the stalks of wharves

Greenwigged with ferny gardens,
A sweep of mermaid hair.

Unburdened in defeat we watched
That neat, shy storm disappear
Over the green sands,
Which are white in our world.

PEGGY BENNETT

The Hen and the Carp

Once, in a roostery
There lived a speckled hen, and when-
Ever she laid an egg this hen
Ecstatically cried:
"O progeny miraculous, particular spectaculous,
What a wonderful hen am I!"

Down in a pond nearby
Perchance a fat and broody carp
Was basking, but her ears were sharp—
She heard Dame Cackle cry:
"O progeny miraculous, particular spectaculous,
What a wonderful hen am I!"

"Ah, Cackle," bubbled she,
"For your single egg, O silly one,
I lay at least a million;
Suppose for each I cried:
'Oh progeny miraculous, particular spectaculous!'
What a hullabaloo there'd be!"

IAN SERRAILLIER

The Oyster

The oyster takes no exercise;
I don't believe she really tries,
  And since she has no legs
I don't see why she should, do you?
Besides, she has a lot to do—
  She lays a million eggs;
At any rate she doesn't stir;
Her food is always brought to her.

But sometimes through her open lips
A horrid little creature slips
  Which simply will not go;
And that annoys the poor old girl,
It means she has to make a pearl—
  It *irritates,* you know;
So, crooning some small requiem,
She turns the worm into a gem.

A. P. HERBERT

Seal

See how he dives
From the rocks with a zoom!
See how he darts
Through his watery room
Past crabs and eels
And green seaweed,
Past fluffs of sandy
Minnow feed!

See how he swims
With a swerve and a twist,
A flip of the flipper,
A flick of the wrist!
Quicksilver-quick,
Softer than spray,
Down he plunges
And sweeps away;
Before you can think,
Before you can utter
Words like "Dill pickle"
Or "Apple butter,"
Back up he swims
Past sting-ray and shark,
Out with a zoom,
A whoop, a bark;
Before you can say
Whatever you wish,
He plops at your side
With a mouthful of fish!

WILLIAM JAY SMITH

River-Mates

I'll be an otter, and I'll let you swim
A mate beside me; we will venture down
A deep, dark river, when the sky above
Is shut of the sun; spoilers are we,
Thick-coated; no dog's tooth can bite at our veins,
With eyes and ears of poachers; deep-earthed ones
Turned hunters; let him slip past
The little vole; my teeth are on an edge
For the King-fish of the River!

I hold him up
The glittering salmon that smells of the sea;
I hold him high and whistle!
Now we go
Back to our earths; we will tear and eat
Sea-smelling salmon; you will tell the cubs
I am the Booty-bringer, I am the Lord
Of the River; the deep, dark, full and flowing River!

PADRAIC COLUM

Lullaby for a Baby Toad

Sleep, my child:
The dark dock leaf
Spreads a tent
To hide your grief.
The thing you saw
In the forest pool
When you bent to drink
In the evening cool
Was a mask that He,
The Wisest Toad,

Gave us to hide
Our precious load—
The jewel that shines
In the flat toad-head
With gracious sapphire
And changing red.
For if, my toadling,
Your face were fair
As the precious jewel
That glimmers there,
Man, the jealous,
Man, the cruel,
Would look at you
And suspect the jewel.
So dry the tears
From your horned eyes,
And eat your supper
Of dew and flies;
Curl in the shade
Of the nettles deep,
Think of your jewel
And go to sleep.

STELLA GIBBONS

To a Fish of the Brook

Why flyest thou away with fear?
Trust me there's naught of danger near,
  I have no wicked hook,
All covered with a snaring bait,
Alas, to tempt thee to thy fate,
  And drag thee from the brook.

Enjoy thy stream, O harmless fish;
And when an angler for his dish,
    Through gluttony's vile sin,
Attempts, a wretch, to pull thee *out,*
God give thee strength, O gentle trout,
    To pull the rascal *in!*

JOHN WOLCOT

Night Song of the Fish

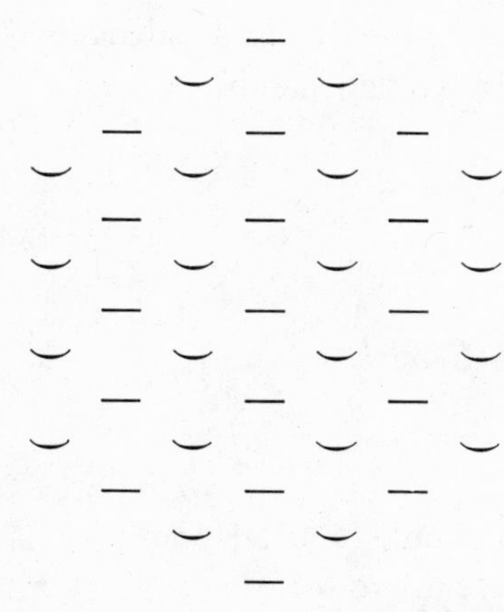

CHRISTIAN MORGENSTERN

Bullfrog

With their lithe long strong legs
Some frogs are able
To thump upon double-
Bass strings though pond-water deadens and clogs.

But you, bullfrog, you pump out
Whole fogs full of horn—a threat
As of a liner looming. True
That, first hearing you
Disgorging your gouts of darkness like a wounded god,
Not utterly fantastical I expected
(As in some antique tale depicted)
A broken-down bull up to its belly in mud,
Sucking black swamp up, belching out black cloud

And a squall of gudgeon and lilies.
A surprise,
To see you, a boy's prize,
No bigger than a rat—all dumb silence
In your little old woman hands.

TED HUGHES

The Maldive Shark

About the Shark, phlegmatical one,
Pale sot of the Maldive sea,
The sleek little pilot-fish, azure and slim,
How alert in attendance be.
From his saw-pit of mouth, from his charnel of maw
They have nothing of harm to dread,
But liquidly glide on his ghastly flank
Or before his Gorgonian head;
Or lurk in the port of serrated teeth
In white triple tiers of glittering gates,
And there find a haven when peril's abroad,
An asylum in jaws of the Fates!
They are friends; and friendly they guide him to prey,

Yet never partake of the treat—
Eyes and brains to the dotard lethargic and dull,
Pale ravener of horrible meat.

HERMAN MELVILLE

The Fish

I caught a tremendous fish
and held him beside the boat
half out of water, with my hook
fast in a corner of his mouth.
He didn't fight.
He hadn't fought at all.
He hung a grunting weight,
battered and venerable
and homely. Here and there
his brown skin hung in strips
like ancient wall-paper,
and its pattern of darker brown
was like wall-paper:
shapes like full-blown roses
stained and lost through age.
He was speckled with barnacles,
fine rosettes of lime
and infested with tiny white sea-lice,
and underneath two or three
rags of green weed hung down.
While his gills were breathing in
the terrible oxygen
—the frightening gills
fresh and crisp with blood,
that can cut so badly—
I thought of the coarse white flesh

packed in like feathers,
the big bones and the little bones,
the dramatic reds and blacks
of his shiny entrails,
and the pink swim-bladder
like a big peony.
I looked into his eyes
which were far larger than mine
but shallower, and yellowed,
the irises backed and packed
with tarnished tinfoil
seen through the lenses
of old scratched isinglass.
They shifted a little, but not
to return my stare.
—It was more like the tipping
of an object toward the light.
I admired his sullen face,
the mechanism of his jaw,
and then I saw
that from his lower lip
—if you could call it a lip—
grim, wet, and weapon-like,
hung five old pieces of fishline,
or four and a wire leader
with the swivel still attached,
with all their five big hooks
grown firmly in his mouth.
A green line, frayed at the end
where he broke it, two heavier lines,
and a fine black thread
still crimped from the strain and snap
when it broke and he got away.
Like medals with their ribbons
frayed and wavering,
a five-haired beard of wisdom

trailing from his aching jaw.
I stared and stared
and victory filled up
the little rented boat,
from the pool of bilge
where oil had spread a rainbow
around the rusted engine
to the bailer rusted orange,
the sun-cracked thwarts,
the oarlocks on their strings,
the gunnels—until everything
was rainbow, rainbow, rainbow!
And I let the fish go.

ELIZABETH BISHOP

Song of Hate for Eels

Oh, the slimy, squirmy, slithery eel!
He swallows your hook with malignant zeal,
He tangles your line and he gums your reel,
The slimy, squirmy, slithery eel.

Oh, the slimy, squirmy, slithery eel!
He cannot be held in a grip of steel,
And when he is dead he is hard to peel,
The slimy, squirmy, slithery eel!

Oh, the slimy, squirmy, slithery eel!
The sorriest catch in the angler's creel;
Who said he was fit for a Christian meal—
The slimy, squirmy, slithery eel!

Oh, the slimy, squirmy, slithery eel!
Malevolent serpent! who dares reveal
What eloquent fishermen say and feel
Concerning the slithery, slimy eel?

ARTHUR GUITERMAN

The Clam

You may leave the clam on the ocean floor,
It's all the same to the clam,
For a hundred thousand years or more,
It's all the same to the clam;
You may carry him home in a gunny sack,
And pour Tabasco on his back,
And use him for a midnight snack,
It's all the same to the clam.

You may carry him 'round to bring you luck,
It's all the same to the clam,
Or use him for a hockey puck,
It's all the same to the clam.
You may dress him in the latest style,
Or pry him open with a file,
The clam will neither frown nor smile,
It's all the same to the clam.

You may call him Bob, or Fran, or Nell,
It's all the same to the clam;

Or make an ashtray from his shell,
  It's all the same to the clam;
You may take him riding on the train,
Or leave him sitting in the rain,
You'll never hear the clam complain,
  It's all the same to the clam.

So the world may stop, or the world may spin,
  It's all the same to the clam;
Or the sky may come a-falling in,
  It's all the same to the clam,
And man may sing his endless song
Of wronging rights and righting wrongs,
The clam just sets and gets along,
  It's all the same to the clam.

SHELLEY SILVERSTEIN

About the Teeth of Sharks

The thing about a shark is—teeth,
One row above, one row beneath.

Now take a close look. Do you find
It has another row behind?

Still closer—here, I'll hold your hat:
Has it a third row behind that?

Now look in and . . . Look out! Oh my,
I'll *never* know now! Well, goodbye.

JOHN CIARDI

Conversion

The shrimp said to the lobster,
"Will you spare me?" said the shrimp.
"Why should I spare you?" said the lobster.
"God gave the water for us to swim around in," said the shrimp.
But the lobster whispered,
"God gave me permission to eat shrimps."

"If you were to swallow me
"I would bite your stomach to shreds," said the shrimp.
"I see," said the lobster, and trembled;
"But why didn't the other shrimps bite my stomach to bits?"
"They were cowards," said the shrimp.

From that day the lobster
Became a vegetarian.

J. T. LILLIE, age 10

The Crayfish

I

The brook wound through the woods behind
The houses, on each trim side was lined

With a wall of orange-brown rocks.
There, I sat with my shoes and socks

Off, under the tall oaks on the bank,
And dangled a piece of string that sank

Its load of bacon slowly down
To the dusty bottom. No sound

Ruffled the water, when I saw
A big crayfish stepping near the raw

Bait. I moved the string to inform
Him of it—back he leaped in a storm

Of cloudy mud. But soon he returned
Clumsy to eat what he had learned

Was easy lunch. He paused to fondle
The soggy dish, then like a bundle

Took it in his heavy pincers. Up,
Up, carefully I drew him up,

Dripping, through his watery sky,
Into my world of green and dry.

II

He started off with a waddling walk
From the ledge, but wanting to talk

I set him back. So he sat there,
His black-reflector eyes in a stare

Of strangeness, while I told and told
How I was a boy, was nine years old,

And liked him. He swayed his feelers round
To show attention at the sound

I made, in the hollow glade of noon.
Wet slow scrapings were all the tune

His clumsy pincers could provide.
For answer. I stroked his armored side,

Brown with yellow speckles like hail
In a dry garden, his plated tail

With its fan-feather-tips, his spiny
Spider-legs (one missing): my tiny

Monster from the stream. And to show
How well I liked him I let him go.

ROBERT WALLACE

Fish

A fish dripping
sparkling drops
of crystal water,
pulled from the lake;
long has it dwelt
in the cool water,
in the cold water
of the lake.

Long has it wandered
to and fro
over the bottom
of the lake
among mysterious
recesses
there in the semi-
light of the water;

now to appear
surprised, aghast,
out of its element
into the day;—
out of the cold
and shining lake
the fish dripping
sparkling water.

W. W. E. ROSS

Slitherers, Creepers, and Hardshells

The Garden Snail

This backyard
cousin
to the octopus
Sees
through two filmy
stems
On his head, at
need
can peer round
Corners, and
so betrays his
huge
Timidity. He
moves on his
single
Elastic foot
seldom,
preferring
Anonymity
to danger,
seems
Often to be
meditating
a very tough
Problem, likes
green leaves
and water.

ROBERT WALLACE

Snake

I saw a young snake glide
Out of a mottled shade
And hang, limp on a stone:
A thin mouth, and a tongue
Stayed, in the still air.

It turned; it drew away;
Its shadow bent in half;
It quickened, and was gone.

I felt my slow blood warm.
I longed to be that thing,
The pure, sensuous form.
And I may be, some time.

THEODORE ROETHKE

Meditations of a Tortoise Dozing under a Rosetree near a Beehive at Noon while a Dog scampers about and a Cuckoo calls from a Distant Wood

So far as I can see,
There is no one like me.

E. V. RIEU

The Snake Trying

The snake trying
to escape the pursuing stick,
with sudden curvings of thin
long body. How beautiful
and graceful are his shapes!
He glides through the water away
from the stroke. O let him go
over the water

into the reeds to hide
without hurt. Small and green
he is harmless even to children.
Along the sand

he lay until observed
and chased away, and now
he vanishes in the ripples
among the green slim reeds.

W. W. E. ROSS

Night Thought of a Tortoise Suffering from Insomnia on a Lawn

The world is very flat—
There is no doubt of that.

E. V. RIEU

A Crocodile

Hard by the lilied Nile I saw
A duskish river-dragon stretched along,
The brown habergeon* of his limbs enamelled
With sanguine almandines* and rainy pearl:
And on his back there lay a young one sleeping,
No bigger than a mouse; with eye like beads,
And a small fragment of its speckled egg
Remaining on its harmless, pulpy snout;
A thing to laugh at, as it gaped to catch
The baulking, merry flies. In the iron jaws
Of the great devil-beast, like a pale soul
Fluttering in rocky hell, lightsomely flew
A snowy trochilus*, with roseate beak
Tearing the hairy leeches from his throat.

THOMAS LOVELL BEDDOES

---

* habergeon: a jacket of mail, armor
* sanguine almandines: the color of blood-red garnets
* trochilus: the "crocodile bird"—a species who live with, and off, crocodiles

Snake

A snake came to my water-trough
On a hot, hot day, and I in pyjamas for the heat,
To drink there.

In the deep, strange-scented shade of the great dark carob-tree
I came down the steps with my pitcher
And must wait, must stand and wait, for there he was at the
  trough before me.

He reached down from a fissure in the earth-wall in the gloom
And trailed his yellow-brown slackness soft-bellied down, over
  the edge of the stone trough
And rested his throat upon the stone bottom,
And where the water had dripped from the tap, in a small
  clearness,
He sipped with his straight mouth,
Softly drank through his straight gums, into his slack long body,
Silently.

Someone was before me at my water-trough,
And I, like a second comer, waiting.

He lifted his head from his drinking, as cattle do,
And looked at me vaguely, as drinking cattle do,
And flickered his two-forked tongue from his lips, and mused
  a moment,
And stooped and drank a little more,
Being earth brown, earth golden from the burning burning
  bowels of the earth
On the day of Sicilian July, with Etna smoking

The voice of my education said to me

He must be killed,
For in Sicily the black, black snakes are innocent, the gold are venomous.

And voices in me said, if you were a man
You would take a stick and break him now, and finish him off.

But I must confess how I liked him,
How glad I was he had come like a guest in quiet, to drink at my water-trough
And depart peaceful, pacified, and thankless,
Into the burning bowels of this earth.

Was it cowardice, that I dared not kill him?
Was it perversity, that I longed to talk to him?
Was it humility, to feel so honored?
I felt so honored.

And yet those voices:
If you were not afraid, you would kill him!

And truly I was afraid, I was most afraid,
But even so, honored still more
That he should seek my hospitality
From out the dark door of the secret earth.

He drank enough
And lifted his head, dreamily, as one who has drunken,
And flickered his tongue like a forked night on the air, so black,
Seeming to lick his lips,
And looked around like a god, unseeing, into the air,
And slowly turned his head,
And slowly, very slowly, as if thrice adream,
Proceeded to draw his slow length curving round
And climb again the broken bank of my wall-face.

And as he put his head into that dreadful hole,
And as he slowly drew up, snake-easing his shoulders, and
entered farther,
A sort of horror, a sort of protest against his withdrawing into
that horrid black hole,
Deliberately going into the blackness, and slowly drawing
himself after,
Overcame me now his back was turned.
I looked round, I put down my pitcher,
I picked up a clumsy log
And threw it at the water-trough with a clatter.

I think it did not hit him,
But suddenly that part of him that was left behind convulsed in
undignified haste,
Writhed like lightning, and was gone
Into the black hole, the earth-lipped fissure in the wall-front,
At which, in the intense still noon, I stared with fascination.

And immediately I regretted it.
I thought how paltry, how vulgar, what a mean act!
I despised myself and the voices of my accursed human education.

And I thought of the albatross,
And I wished he would come back, my snake.

For he seemed to me again like a king,
Like a king in exile, uncrowned in the underworld,
Now due to be crowned again.

And so, I missed my chance with one of the lords
Of life.
And I have something to expiate;
A pettiness.

D. H. LAWRENCE

The Hare and the Tortoise

"You can't race me," said Johnny the Hare,
"Before you've started I'll be there.
  From the barley field
  To the Farmer's barn
I'll lick you, Sammy, fair and square."

Sammy the Tortoise said, "Wait and see!"
Away he crawled to his family (three),
  Clarence, Creeper,
  And Marmaduke—
They were all alike as like could be.

"I've entered, mi-lads, for a steeplechase.
I can't leap over the land apace,
  But if four of us run
  Disguised as one,
I guess I can win this jolly old race.

"Clarence, you hide by the green duck pond;
Creeper, in pigsty a mile behind.

"The starting line, yon barley stook,
Is just the place for you, Marmaduke.

"And me? I'll hide where I'm needed most
A nose and a half from a winning-post."

Marm and Johnny lined up at the start.
"This race," said Johnny, "is really a farce.
  The wheat I sow
  From my bag as I go
Will be ready to cut by the time you pass."

Bang!—they're off! The Hare at a bound
Rocketed over the billowy ground.
  But when he skirted
  The green duck pond,
The Tortoise was only a yard behind.

And when he came to the old pigsty
They were almost neck and neck—O my!

Poor Johnny the Hare, his field half sown,
Threw off his bag and continued alone,
  Drooping and dropping
  And stooping and stopping
And puffing and panting, terribly blown.

Ten yards from the tape he grew a bit bolder
And casting a careless eye over shoulder,
  "Sam, are you there?"
  Said Johnny the Hare.
"I've won!" said the Tortoise, in front, "I told yer."

Farmer and friends were holding the tape,
And *there* was Sammy, all bowing and scrape,
  His head held high—
  What a sock in the eye
For Johnny, who stands with his mouth agape.

"Well done!" said the farmer. "And now, methinks,
'Tis proper to offer you eats and drinks.
  Will you join me, both?"
  "No!" with an oath
Said Johnny the Hare, and home he slinks.

But later on back to the farm he hobbled;
His limbs were still limp, and his brain was fuddled.
As he peered through the window he babbled and

Bubbled:
"*Four* Sammies I see
A-sipping their tea!
Strikes me
I galloped so fast I'm seeing twice double."

IAN SERRAILLIER

A Narrow Fellow in the Grass

A narrow fellow in the grass
Occasionally rides;
You may have met him,—did you not?
His notice sudden is.

The grass divides as with a comb,
A spotted shaft is seen;
And then it closes at your feet
And opens further on.

He likes a boggy acre,
A floor too cool for corn.
Yet when a child, & barefoot,
I more than once, at morn,

Have passed, I thought a whip-lash
Unbraiding in the sun,—
When, stooping to secure it,
It wrinkled, and was gone.

Several of nature's people
I know, and they know me;
I feel for them a transport
Of cordiality;

But never met this fellow,
Attended or alone,
Without a tighter breathing,
And zero at the bone.

EMILY DICKINSON

The Snail

To grass, or leaf, or fruit, or wall,
The Snail sticks close, nor fears to fall,
As if he grew there, house and all
Together.

Within that house secure he hides,
When danger imminent betides
Of storm, or other harm besides,
Of weather.

Give but his horns the slightest touch,
His self-collecting power is such,
He shrinks into his house, with much
Displeasure.

Where'er he dwells, he dwells alone,
Except himself has chattels none,
Well satisfied to be his own
Whole treasure.

Thus hermit-like his life he leads,
Nor partner of his banquet needs,
And if he meets one, only feeds
The faster.

Who seeks him must be worse than blind
(He and his house are so combin'd)
If, finding it, he fails to find
        Its master.

WILLIAM COWPER

The Snail

At sunset, when the night-dews fall,
Out of the ivy on the wall
With horns outstretched and pointed tail
Comes the grey and noiseless snail.
On ivy stems she clambers down,
Carrying her house of brown.
Safe in the dark, no greedy eye
Can her tender body spy,
While she herself, a hungry thief,
Searches out the freshest leaf.
She travels on as best she can
Like a toppling caravan.

JAMES REEVES

To the Snake

Green Snake, when I hung you round my neck
and stroked your cold, pulsing throat
    as you hissed to me, glinting
arrowy gold scales, and I felt
    the weight of you on my shoulders,
and the whispering silver of your dryness
    sounded close at my ears—

Green Snake—I swore to my companions that certainly
  you were harmless! But truly
I had no certainty, and no hope, only desiring
  to hold you, for that joy, which left
a long wake of pleasure, as the leaves moved
and you faded into the pattern
of grass and shadows, and I returned
smiling and haunted, to a dark morning.

DENISE LEVERTOV

Soliloquy of a Tortoise on Revisiting the Lettuce Beds after an Interval of One Hour while supposed to be Sleeping in a Clump of Blue Hollyhocks

One cannot have enough
Of this delicious stuff!

E. V. RIEU

Upon the Snail

She goes but softly, but she goeth sure;
She stumbles not as stronger creatures do:
Her journey's shorter, so she may endure
Better than they which do much further go.

She makes no noise, but stilly seizeth on
The flower or herb appointed for her food,
The which she quietly doth feed upon,
While others range, and gare,* but find no good.

And though she doth but very softly go,
However 'tis not fast, nor slow, but sure;
And certainly they that do travel so,
The prize they do aim at, they do procure.

JOHN BUNYAN

The Chameleon

The chameleon changes his color;
  He can look like a tree or a wall;
He is timid and shy, and he hates to be seen,
So he simply sits down in the grass and goes green,
  And pretends he is nothing at all.

I wish I could change my complexion
  To purple or orange or red;
I wish I could look like the arm of a chair
So nobody ever would know I was there,
  When they wanted to put me to bed.

* gare: become excited

I wish I could be a chameleon,
And look like a lily or rose;
I'd lie on the apples and peaches and pears,
But not on Aunt Margaret's horrible chairs—
I should have to be careful of those.

The chameleon's life is confusing,
He is used to adventure and pain;
But if ever he sat on Aunt Maggie's cretonne
And noticed what curious colors he'd gone,
I don't think he'd do it again.

A. P. HERBERT

Dogs

Tom's Little Dog

Tom told his dog called Tim to beg,
And up at once he sat,
His two clear amber eyes fixed fast,
His haunches on his mat.

Tom poised a lump of sugar on
His nose; then, "Trust!" says he;
Stiff as a guardsman sat his Tim;
Never a hair stirred he.

"Paid for!" says Tom; and in a trice
Up jerked that moist black nose;
A snap of teeth, a crunch, a munch,
And down the sugar goes!

WALTER DE LA MARE

The Dog from Malta

He came from Malta; and Eumêlus says
He had no better dog in all his days.
We called him Bull; he went into the dark.
Along those roads we cannot hear him bark.

TYMNÈS
(Translated from the Greek by EDMUND BLUNDEN)

Our Lucy (1956-1960)

1.

Small as a fox and like
a little fox but black,
  our Lucy's white teeth grin
  among the rushes green.

The feathers of her plume
flutter in the warm
  winds that fitfully blow
  from the Gulf of Mexico,

and like a machine-gun
her barking through the pine
  echoes where people have
  set foot on our grove:

"Quiet, Lucy. They
may bring us news today,
  or if thieves they may
  drop something on their way."

2.

She was a happy little dog
because she loved three things only,
us and food and to go barking
forth in the world, feathers high:
of these she had a plenty till
the car hit her at Eagle's Bridge;
died without pain in Sally's arms
blood slowly dripping from her jaws,
we buried her with a borrowed shovel
a cairn of stones on the river bank

—she who leaped with joy to greet us
and enlivened us with her lovely spirit,
how suddenly! there she was
and now is not in our empty house.

PAUL GOODMAN

The Turkish Trench Dog

Night held me as I scrawled and scrambled near
The Turkish lines. Above, the mocking stars
Silvered the curving parapet, and clear
Cloud-latticed beams o'erflecked the land with bars;
I, crouching, lay between
Tense-listening armies, peering through the night,
Twin giants bound by tentacles unseen.
Here in dim-shadowed light
I saw him, as a sudden movement turned
His eyes towards me, glowing eyes that burned
A moment ere his snuffling muzzle found
My trail; and then as serpents mesmerize
He chained me with those unrelenting eyes,
That muscle-sliding rhythm, knit and bound
In spare-limbed symmetry, those perfect jaws
And soft-approaching pitter-patter paws.
Nearer and nearer like a wolf he crept—
That moment had my swift revolver leapt—
But terror seized me, terror born of shame,
Brought brooding revelation. For he came
As one who offers comradeship deserved,
An open ally of the human race,
And sniffling at my prostrate form unnerved
He licked my face!

GEOFFREY DEARMER

Wonder

Collie puppies in a dooryard,
Wheeling along lopsided,
So hard to manage those hind legs,
Standing, blue eyes on nothing,
Noses twitching,
Stubby tails in the air,
Trying to remember what they are thinking about:

Fat puppies that forget everything,
Even the terrible
White teeth their mother yops at them
When she eats her supper:

Fat puppies full of wonder
At round holes where spiders live,
At the wide wings of a yellow butterfly,
And lifting shrill voices of wonder
At the stranger who leans over their gate
Making uncouth noises.

BERNARD RAYMUND

Pourquoi

O Jean Baptiste, pourquoi,
O Jean Baptiste, pourquoi,
O Jean Baptiste,
Pourquoi you greased
My little dog's nose with tar?

Your little dog had catarrh,
Your little dog had catarrh,
And that was the reason
Why I have greasen
Your little dog's nose with tar.

O Jean Baptiste, I'm glad
O Jean Baptiste, I'm glad
O Jean Baptiste,
I'm glad you greased
My little dog's nose with tar.

ANONYMOUS

Lone Dog

I'm a lean dog, a keen dog, a wild dog, and lone;
I'm a rough dog, a tough dog, hunting on my own;
I'm a bad dog, a mad dog, teasing silly sheep;
I love to sit and bay the moon, to keep fat souls from sleep.

I'll never be a lap dog, licking dirty feet,
A sleek dog, a meek dog, cringing for my meat,
Not for me the fireside, the well-filled plate,
But shut door, and sharp stone, and cuff and kick and hate.

Not for me the other dogs, running by my side,
Some have run a short while, but none of them would bide.
O mine is still the lone trail, the hard trail, the best,
Wide wind, and wild stars, and hunger of the quest!

IRENE RUTHERFORD MCLEOD

Tim, an Irish Terrier

It's wonderful dogs they're breeding now:
Small as a flea or large as a cow
But my old lad Tim he'll never be bet
By any dog that ever he met.
"Come on," says he, "for I'm not kilt yet."

No matter the size of the dog he'll meet,
Tim trails his coat the length o' the street.
D'ye mind his scars an' his ragged ear,
The like of a Dublin Fusilier?
He's a massacree dog that knows no fear.

But he'd stick to me till his latest breath;
An' he'd go with me to the gates of death.
He'd wait for a thousand years, maybe,
Scratching the door an' whining for me
If myself were inside in Purgatary.

So I laugh when I hear thim make it plain
That dogs and men never meet again.
For all their talk who'd listen to thim,
With the soul in the shining eyes of him?
Would God be wasting a dog like Tim?

W. M. LETTS

The Night Hunt

In the morning, in the dark,
When the stars begin to blunt,
By the wall of Barna Park
Dogs I heard and saw them hunt.
All the parish dogs were there,
All the dogs for miles around,
Teeming up behind a hare,
In the dark, without a sound.

How I heard I scarce can tell—
'Twas a patter in the grass—
And I did not see them well
Come across the dark and pass;
Yet I saw them and I knew
Spearman's dog and Spellman's dog
And, beside my own dog too,
Leamy's from the Island Bog.

In the morning when the sun
Burnished all the green to gorse,
I went out to take a run
Round the bog upon my horse;
And my dog that had been sleeping
In the heat beside the door
Left his yawning and went leaping
On a hundred yards before.

Through the village street we passed—
Not a dog there raised a snout—
Through the street and out at last
On the white bog road and out
Over Barna Park full pace,

Over to the Silver Stream,
Horse and dog in happy race,
Rider between thought and dream.

By the stream at Leamy's house,
Lay a dog—my pace I curbed—
But our coming did not rouse
Him from drowsing undisturbed;
And my dog, as unaware
Of the other, dropped beside
And went running by me there
With my horse's slackened stride.

Yet by something, by a twitch
Of the sleeper's eye, a look
From the runner, something which
Little chords of feeling shook,
I was conscious that a thought
Shuddered through the silent deep
Of a secret—I had caught
Something I had known in sleep.

THOMAS MacDONAGH

Daley's Dorg Wattie

"You can talk about yer sheep dorgs," said the man from Allan's Creek,
"But I know a dorg that simply knocked 'em bandy!—
Do whatever you would show him, and you'd hardly need to speak;
Owned by Daley, drover cove in Jackandandy.

"We was talkin' in the parlour, me and Daley, quiet like,
When a blow-fly starts a-buzzin' round the ceilin',

Up gets Daley, and he says to me, 'You wait a minute, Mike,
And I'll show you what a dorg he is at heelin'.'

"And an empty pickle-bottle was a-standin' on the shelf,
Daley takes it down and puts it on the table,
And he bets me drinks that blinded dorg would do it by himself—
And I didn't think as how as he was able!

"Well, he shows the dorg the bottle, and he points up to the fly,
And he shuts the door, and says to him—'Now Wattle!'
And in less than fifteen seconds, spare me days, it ain't a lie,
That there dorg had got that inseck in the bottle."

W. T. GOODGE

The Dog's Cold Nose

When Noah, perceiving 'twas time to embark,
Persuaded the creatures to enter the Ark,
The dog, with a friendliness truly sublime,
Assisted in herding them. Two at a time
He drove in the elephants, zebras and gnus
Until they were packed like a boxful of screws,
The cat in the cupboard, the mouse on the shelf,
The bug in the crack; then he backed in himself.
But such was the lack of available space
He couldn't tuck all of him into the place;
So after the waters had flooded the plain
And down from the heavens fell blankets of rain
He stood with his muzzle thrust out through the door
The whole forty days of that terrible pour!
Because of which drenching, zoologists hold,
The nose of a healthy dog always is cold!

ARTHUR GUITERMAN

The Woodman's Dog

Shaggy, and lean, and shrewd, with pointed ears
And tail cropped short, half lurcher and half cur—
His dog attends him. Close behind his heel
Now creeps he slow; and now with many a frisk
Wide-scampering, snatches up the drifted snow
With ivory teeth, or plows it with his snout;
Then shakes his powdered coat and barks for joy.

WILLIAM COWPER

The House Dog's Grave

(HAIG, AN ENGLISH BULLDOG)

I've changed my ways a little; I cannot now
Run with you in the evenings along the shore,
Except in a kind of dream; and you, if you dream a moment,
You see me there.

So leave awhile the paw-marks on the front door
Where I used to scratch to go out or in,
And you'd soon open; leave on the kitchen floor
The marks of my drinking-pan.

I cannot lie by your fire as I used to do
On the warm stone,
Nor at the foot of your bed; no, all the nights through
I lie alone.

But your kind thought has laid me less than six feet
Outside your window where firelight so often plays,
And where you sit to read—and I fear often grieving for me—
Every night your lamplight lies on my place.

You, man and woman, live so long, it is hard
To think of you ever dying.
A little dog would get tired, living so long.
I hope that when you are lying

Under the ground like me your lives will appear
As good and joyful as mine.
No, dears, that's too much hope: you are not so well cared for
As I have been.

And never have known the passionate undivided
Fidelities that I knew.
Your minds are perhaps too active, too many-sided . . .
But to me you were true.

You were never masters, but friends. I was your friend.
I loved you well, and was loved. Deep love endures
To the end and far past the end. If this is my end,
I am not lonely. I am not afraid. I am still yours.

ROBINSON JEFFERS

Old Dog Tray

The morn of life is past,
And ev'ning comes at last;
It brings me a dream of a once happy day,
Of merry forms I've seen
Upon the village green,
Sporting with my old dog Tray.
Old dog Tray's ever faithful;
Grief cannot drive him away;
He's gentle, he is kind,
I'll never, never find
A better friend than old dog Tray.

The forms I called my own
Have vanish'd one by one,
The lov'd ones, the dear ones have all
pass'd away;
Their happy smiles have flown,
Their gentle voices gone,
I've nothing left but old dog Tray.
Old dog Tray's ever faithful;
Grief cannot drive him away;
He's gentle, he is kind,
I'll never, never find
A better friend than old dog Tray.

When thoughts recall the past,
His eyes are on me cast,
I know that he feels what my breaking
heart would say;
Although he cannot speak,
I'll vainly, vainly seek
A better friend than old dog Tray.
Old dog Tray's ever faithful;
Grief cannot drive him away;
He's gentle, he is kind,
I'll never, never find
A better friend than old dog Tray.

STEPHEN FOSTER

Hector the Dog

Shake hands with Hector the dog, for Hector is
Not as he appears to be. He gives
A false impression by his yellow glare;
His glare is the glare of love, by love he lives.

Hector's well-bred eye is glassy with love;
He sees our presence and sees nothing more.
If locked behind, he will go loudly mad,
Crash through a window or break down the door.

And this has left him as scarred as some old courtier
Who carries the seals of devotion on body and head.
He is always there. The king complains about it.
But he'll miss him once the old dog's dead.

KATE BARNES

Mick

Mick my mongrel-O
Lives in a bungalow,
Painted green with a round doorway.
With an eye for cats
And a nose for rats
He lies on his threshold half the day.
He buries his bones
By the rockery stones,
And never, oh never, forgets the place.
Ragged and thin
From his tail to his chin,
He looks at you with a sideways face.
Dusty and brownish,
Wicked and clownish,
He'll win no prize at the County Show.
But throw him a stick,
And up jumps Mick,
And right through the flower-beds see him go!

JAMES REEVES

Night Song

On moony nights the dogs bark shrill
Down the valley and up the hill.

There's one who is angry to behold
The moon so unafraid and cold,
That makes the earth as bright as day,
But yet unhappy, dead, and grey.

Another in his strawy lair,
Says: "Who's a-howling over there?
By heavens I will stop him soon
From interfering with the moon."

So back he barks, with throat upthrown;
"You leave our moon, our moon alone."
And other distant dogs respond
Beyond the fields, beyond, beyond.

FRANCES CORNFORD

Dog, Midwinter

This dog barking at me now—
do I really bother him
or is he acting out
the old faithful watch-dog routine?

Or (and I hope it's this)
is he so lonely locked up
in the snow-filled yard that the sight
of another living thing stirs him?

For I can truly say
I'm as lonely now
as you, dog, so
speaking for both of us
bark your crazy head off.

RAYMOND SOUSTER

The Ambiguous Dog

The dog beneath the cherry tree
Has ways that sorely puzzle me:

Behind, he wags a friendly tail;
Before, his growl would turn you pale!

His meaning isn't plain and clear;
Oh, is the wag or growl sincere?

I think I'd better not descend;
His bite is at the growly end.

ARTHUR GUITERMAN

Our Dumb Friends

My home is a haven for one who enjoys
The clamor of children and ear-splitting noise
From a number of dogs who are always about,
And who want to come in and, once in, to go out.
Whenever I settle to read by the fire,
Some dog will develop an urge to retire,
And I'm constantly opening and shutting the door

For a dog to depart or, as mentioned before,
For a dog to arrive who, politely admitted,
Will make a bee-line for the chair I've just quitted.
Our friends may be dumb, but my house is a riot,
Where I cannot sit still and can never be quiet.

RALPH WOTHERSPOON

Denise

Come here, Denise!
Come let us find a little patch of sun
And meditate a measurement of time.

I have outlived five dogs:
Hector and Hercules,
Genghis the golden,
The fashionable Pamplemousse,
And, lately, Hans of Weimar,
Hans of the amber eyes.

You are my last, Denise;
Life is but one dog more,
Denise, my raisin-bread Dalmatian,
Denise of the delicate crossed paws.

ROBERT BEVERLY HALE

pete at the seashore

i ran along the yellow sand
and made the sea gulls fly
i chased them down the waters edge
i chased them up the sky

i ran so hard i ran so fast
i left the spray behind
i chased the flying flecks of foam
and i outran the wind

an airplane sailing overhead
climbed when it heard me bark
i yelped and leapt right at the sun
until the sky grew dark

some little children on the beach
threw sticks and ran with me
o master let us go again
and play beside the sea

pete the pup

DON MARQUIS

Cats

Cat!

Cat!
Scat!
After her, after her,
Sleeky flatterer,
Spitfire chatterer,
Scatter her, scatter her
Off her mat!
Wuff!
Wuff!
Treat her rough!
Git her, git her,
Whiskery spitter!
Catch her, catch her,
Green-eyed scratcher!
Slathery
Slithery
Hisser,
Don't miss her!
Run till you're dithery,
Hithery
Thithery
Pftts! pftts!
How she spits!
Spitch! Spatch!
Can't she scratch!
Scritching the bark

Of the sycamore-tree,
She's reached her ark
And's hissing at me
  Pftts! pftts!
  Wuff! wuff!
    Scat,
    Cat!
    That's
    That!

ELEANOR FARJEON

Cat & the Weather

Cat takes a look at the weather:
snow;
puts a paw on the sill;
his perch is piled, is a pillow.

Shape of his pad appears:
will it dig? No,
not like sand,
like his fur almost.

But licked, not liked:
too cold.
Insects are flying, fainting down.
He'll try

to bat one against the pane.
They have no body and no buzz,
and now his feet are wet;
it's a puzzle.

Shakes each leg,
then shakes his skin
to get the white flies off;
looks for his tail,

tells it to come on in
by the radiator.
World's turned queer
somehow: all white,

no smell. Well, here
inside it's still familiar.
He'll go to sleep until
it puts itself right.

MAY SWENSON

That Cat

The cat that comes to my window sill
When the moon looks cold and the night is still—
He comes in a frenzied state alone
With a tail that stands like a pine tree cone,
And says: "I have finished my evening lark,
And I think I can hear a hound dog bark.
My whiskers are froze 'nd stuck to my chin.
I do wish you'd git up and let me in."
That cat gits in.

But if in the solitude of the night
He doesn't appear to be feeling right,
And rises and stretches and seeks the floor,
And some remote corner he would explore,

And doesn't feel satisfied just because
There's no good spot for to sharpen his claws,
And meows and canters uneasy about
Beyond the least shadow of any doubt
That cat gits out.

BEN KING

The Lost Cat

She took a last and simple meal when there were none to see her steal—
A jug of cream upon the shelf, a fish prepared for dinner;
And now she walks a distant street with delicately sandalled feet,
And no one gives her much to eat or weeps to see her thinner.

O my belovèd come again, come back in joy, come back in pain,
To end our searching with a mew, or with a purr our grieving;
And you shall have for lunch or tea whatever fish swim in the sea
And all the cream that's meant for me—and not a word of thieving!

E. V. RIEU

The Kitten

The trouble with a kitten is
THAT
Eventually it becomes a
CAT.

OGDEN NASH

Diamond Cut Diamond

Two cats
One up a tree
One under the tree
The cat up a tree is he
The cat under the tree is she
The tree is witch elm, just incidentally.
He takes no notice of she, she takes no notice of he.
He stares at the woolly clouds passing, she stares at the tree.
There's been a lot written about cats, by Old Possum, Yeats and Company
But not Alfred de Musset or Lord Tennyson or Poe or anybody
Wrote about one cat under, and one cat up, a tree.
God knows why this should be left for me
Except I like cats as cats be
Especially one cat up
And one under
A witch elm
Tree

EWART MILNE

On a Night of Snow

Cat, if you go outdoors you must walk in the snow,
You will come back with little white shoes on your feet,
Little white slippers of snow that have heels of sleet.
Stay by the fire, my Cat. Lie still, do not go.
See how the flames are leaping and hissing low,
I will bring you a saucer of milk like a marguerite,
So white and so smooth, so spherical and so sweet—
Stay with me, Cat. Out-doors the wild winds blow.

Out-doors the wild winds blow, Mistress, and dark is the night.
Strange voices cry in the trees, intoning strange lore
And more than cats move, lit by our eyes' green light,
On silent feet where the meadow grasses hang hoar—
Mistress, there are portents abroad of magic and might,
And things that are yet to be done. Open the door!

ELIZABETH COATSWORTH

The Kitten and the Falling Leaves

See the Kitten on the wall,
Sporting with the leaves that fall,
Withered leaves—one, two and three—
From the lofty elder-tree!
Through the calm and frosty air
Of this morning bright and fair,
Eddying round and round they sink
Softly, slowly: one might think,
From the motions that are made,
Every little leaf conveyed
Sylph or Faery hither tending,
To this lower world descending,
Each invisible and mute,
In his wavering parachute.

—But the Kitten, how she starts,
Crouches, stretches paws, and darts!
First at one, and then its fellow
Just as light and just as yellow.
There are many now—now one—
Now they stop and there are none:

What intenseness of desire
In her upward eye of fire!

With a tiger-leap half way
Now she meets the coming prey,
Lets it go as fast, and then
Has it in her power again:

Now she works with three or four,
Like an Indian conjurer;
Quick as he in feats of art,
Far beyond in joy of heart.
Were her antics played in the eye
Of a thousand standers-by,
Clapping hands with shout and stare,
What would little Tabby care
For the plaudits of the crowd?

WILLIAM WORDSWORTH

Poem

As the cat
climbed over
the top of

the jamcloset
first the right
forefoot

carefully
then the hind
stepped down

into the pit of
the empty
flowerpot

WILLIAM CARLOS WILLIAMS

Death of the Cat

Alas! Mowler, the children's pride,
Has slipped on a water-butt, tumbled inside
And died.

The seamstress on her sewing machine
Stitched a shroud of satin sheen.

The carpenter hammered and planed a coffin
Of seasoned oak without a knot in.

The sexton—he loved dear Mowler well—
Mournfully, mournfully tolled the bell.

Few were the prayers the parson spoke.
All he could do, poor fellow, was choke.

But saddest of all in the funeral train
Were the children. Deep were their sorrow and pain,

For they knew, as they followed the churchyard through,
They'd never set eyes on Mowler again.

In silence behind the coffin they stepped,
Solemnly, slowly. Everyone wept

Except
The little mice hid in the hedge—not they!

'Twas not *their* hearts that bled.
"Let's out and play,"
They cried. "Oh, spread
The butter thick on the bread!

Dance in cream cheese right up to our knees,
For the cat is dead!
Hooray!
The cat
            is
                  dead!"

IAN SERRAILLIER

My Cat Jeoffry

For I will consider my Cat Jeoffry.
For he is the servant of the Living God, duly and daily serving him.
For at the first glance of the glory of God in the East he worships in his way.
For is this done by wreathing his body seven times round with elegant quickness.
For then he leaps up to catch the musk, which is the blessing of God upon his prayer.
For he rolls upon prank to work it in.
For having done duty, and received blessing he begins to consider himself.
For this he performs in ten degrees.
For first he looks upon his fore-paws to see if they are clean.
For secondly he kicks up behind to clear away there.
For thirdly he works it upon stretch with the fore-paws extended.
For fourthly he sharpens his paws by wood.
For fifthly he washes himself.
For sixthly he rolls upon wash.
For seventhly he fleas himself, that he may not be interrupted upon the beat.
For eighthly he rubs himself against a post.
For ninthly he looks up for his instructions.

For tenthly he goes in quest of food.
For having consider'd God and himself he will consider his neighbour.
For if he meets another cat he will kiss her in kindness.
For when he takes his prey he plays with it to give it chance.
For one mouse in seven escapes by his dallying.
For when his day's work is done his business more properly begins.
For [he] keeps the Lord's watch in the night against the adversary.
For he counteracts the powers of darkness by his electrical skin and glaring eyes.
For he counteracts the Devil, who is death, by brisking about the life.
For in his morning orisons he loves the sun and the sun loves him.
For he is of the tribe of Tiger.
For the Cherub Cat is a term of the Angel Tiger.
For he has the subtlety and hiss of a serpent, which in goodness he suppresses.
For he will not do destruction, if he is well-fed, neither will he spit without provocation.
For he purrs in thankfulness, when God tells him he's a good Cat.
For he is an instrument for the children to learn benevolence upon.
For every house is incomplete without him and a blessing is lacking in the spirit.
For the Lord commanded Moses concerning the cats at the departure of the Children of Israel from Egypt.
For every family had one cat at least in the bag.
For the English Cats are the best in Europe.
For he is the cleanest in the use of his fore-paws of any quadrupede.
For the dexterity of his defence is an instance of the love of God to him exceedingly.
For he is the quickest to his mark of any creature.

For he is tenacious of his point.
For he is a mixture of gravity and waggery.
For he knows that God is his Saviour.
For there is nothing sweeter than his peace when at rest.
For there is nothing brisker than his life when in motion.
For he is of the Lord's poor and so indeed is he called by
benevolence perpetually—Poor Jeoffry! poor Jeoffry! the rat
has bit thy throat.
For I bless the name of the Lord Jesus that Jeoffry is better.
For the divine spirit comes about his body to sustain it in
complete cat.
For his tongue is exceeding pure so that it has in purity what it
wants in music.
For he is docile and can learn certain things.
For he can set up with gravity which is patience upon
approbation.
For he can fetch and carry, which is patience in employment.
For he can jump over a stick which is patience upon proof
positive.
For he can spraggle upon waggle at the word of command.
For he can jump from an eminence into his master's bosom.
For he can catch the cork and toss it again.
For he is hated by the hypocrite and miser.
For the former is afraid of detection.
For the latter refuses the charge.
For he camels his back to bear the first notion of business.
For he is good to think on, if a man would express himself neatly.
For he made a great figure in Egypt for his signal services.
For he killed the Icneumon-rat very pernicious by land.
For his ears are so acute that they sting again.
For from this proceeds the passing quickness of his attention.
For by stroking of him I have found out electricity.
For I perceived God's light about him both wax and fire.
For the Electrical fire is the spiritual substance, which God sends
from heaven to sustain the bodies both of man and beast.
For God has blessed him in the variety of his movements.

For, tho he cannot fly, he is an excellent clamberer.
For his motions upon the face of the earth are more than any other quadrupede.
For he can tread to all the measures upon the music.
For he can swim for life.
For he can creep.

CHRISTOPHER SMART

Cat

The black cat yawns.
Opens her jaws,
Stretches her legs,
And shows her claws.

Then she gets up
And stands on four
Long stiff legs
And yawns some more.

She shows her sharp teeth,
She stretches her lip,
Her slice of a tongue
Turns up at the tip.

Lifting herself
On her delicate toes,
She arches her back
As high as it goes.

She lets herself down
With particular care,
And pads away
With her tail in the air.

MARY BRITTON MILLER

Macavity: The Mystery Cat

Macavity's a Mystery Cat: he's called the Hidden Paw—
For he's the master criminal who can defy the Law.
He's the bafflement of Scotland Yard, the Flying Squad's despair:
For when they reach the scene of crime—*Macavity's not there!*

Macavity, Macavity, there's no one like Macavity,
He's broken every human law, he breaks the law of gravity.
His powers of levitation would make a fakir stare,
And when you reach the scene of crime—*Macavity's not there!*
You may seek him in the basement, you may look up in the air—
But I tell you once and once again, *Macavity's not there!*

Macavity's a ginger cat, he's very tall and thin;
You would know him if you saw him, for his eyes are sunken in.
His brow is deeply lined with thought, his head is highly domed;
His coat is dusty from neglect, his whiskers are uncombed.
He sways his head from side to side, with movements like a
snake;
And when you think he's half asleep, he's always wide awake.

Macavity, Macavity, there's no one like Macavity,
For he's a fiend in feline shape, a monster of depravity.
You may meet him in a by-street, you may see him in the square—
But when a crime's discovered, then *Macavity's not there!*

He's outwardly respectable. (They say he cheats at cards.)
And his footprints are not found in any file of Scotland Yard's.
And when the larder's looted, or the jewel-case is rifled,
Or when the milk is missing, or another Peke's been stifled,
Or the greenhouse glass is broken, and the trellis past repair—
Ay, there's the wonder of the thing! *Macavity's not there!*

And when the Foreign Office find a Treaty's gone astray,
Or the Admiralty lose some plans and drawings by the way,
There may be a scrap of paper in the hall or on the stair—
But it's useless to investigate—*Macavity's not there!*
And when the loss has been disclosed, the Secret Service say:
"It *must* have been Macavity!"—but he's a mile away.
You'll be sure to find him resting, or a-licking of his thumbs,
Or engaged in doing complicated long division sums.

Macavity, Macavity, there's no one like Macavity,
There never was a Cat of such deceitfulness and suavity.
He always has an alibi, and one or two to spare:
At whatever time the deed took place—MACAVITY WASN'T
THERE!
And they say that all the Cats whose wicked deeds are widely
known
(I might mention Mungojerrie, I might mention Griddlebone)
Are nothing more than agents for the Cat who all the time
Just controls their operations: the Napoleon of Crime!

T. S. ELIOT

Five Eyes

In Hans' old mill his three black cats
Watch his bins for the thieving rats.
Whisker and claw, they crouch in the night,
Their five eyes smouldering green and bright:
Squeaks from the flour sacks, squeaks from where
The cold wind stirs on the empty stair,
Squeaking and scampering, everywhere.
Then down they pounce, now in, now out,
At whiskering tail, and sniffing snout;
While lean old Hans he snores away
Till peep of light at break of day;
Then up he climbs to his creaking mill,
Out come his cats all grey with meal—
Jekkel, and Jessup, and one-eyed Jill.

WALTER DE LA MARE

The Cats

In Sycamore Square
At the crack of dawn
The white cats play
On the grey green lawn;
One is the owner
Of Number Three
And the other pretends
To belong to me.
Slowly over
The dew-soaked grass

Their low tense bodies
Like serpents pass,
And each imperceptible
Smooth advance
Is an intricate step
In a mystic dance,
Which ends in the cat
From Number Three
Rushing quite suddenly
Up a tree.
While mine walks off
With a dignified air
To the other end of Sycamore Square.
But nobody yet has ever found out
What in the world
The game's about.

JAN STRUTHER

Cats

On the last Mayday morning my cat brought
Into the world six darling little kittens,
May-kittens, all pure white with black tail-tippings.
Indeed, it was a decorative childbed.
The cook, however—cooks are savage beings,
And human kindness grows not in a kitchen—
Five of the six she meant to take and drown them,
Five white, but tipped-with-black-tail, Mayday kittens
This monstrous woman had marked down to kill.
I took her down a peg. May heaven bless
Me for my human feeling! The dear kittens,
They grew and grew, and in a short while ventured
With high tails walking over court and hearth;

Yes, as the cook sadistically noticed,
They grew and grew, and nightly at her window
They practised out their darling little voices.
I, for my part, as I now saw them growing,
I prized myself and my humanity.

A year is round, and they are cats, those kittens,
And it is Mayday! How can I describe it,
The scene that now enacts itself before me?
My whole house, from the cellar to the gable,
Its every single corner is a childbed!
Here one is lying, there another kitten,
In cupboards, baskets, under stairs and table;
The old cat even—no, I dare not say it,
Lies in the cook's own maiden-modest bed.
And each, yes, each one of the seven she-cats,
Has seven, think, has seven youthful kittens,
May-kittens, all pure white with black tail-tippings.
The cook is raving. I can set no bounds
To the blind anger of this dreadful female.
She will go out and drown all nine-and-forty!
Yet I myself, my head recoils from it:
O human kindness, how can I preserve you?
What can I do with six-and-fifty cats?

THEODOR STORM
(Translated from the German by VERNON WATKINS)

The Cat and the Moon

The cat went here and there
And the moon spun round like a top,
And the nearest kin of the moon,
The creeping cat, looked up.
Black Minnaloushe stared at the moon,

For, wander and wail as he would,
The pure cold light in the sky
Troubled his animal blood.
Minnaloushe runs in the grass
Lifting his delicate feet.
Do you dance, Minnaloushe, do you dance?
When two close kindred meet,
What better than call a dance?
Maybe the moon may learn,
Tired of that courtly fashion,
A new dance turn.
Minnaloushe creeps through the grass
From moonlit place to place,
The sacred moon overhead
Has taken a new phase.
Does Minnaloushe know that his pupils
Will pass from change to change,
And that from round to crescent,
From crescent to round they range?
Minnaloushe creeps through the grass
Alone, important and wise,
And lifts to the changing moon
His changing eyes.

WILLIAM BUTLER YEATS

Cat on Couch

My cat, washing her tail's tip, is a whorl
Of white shell,
As perfect as a fan
In full half-moon . . . Next moment she's a hare:
The muzzle softens, rounds, goes dumb, and one

Tall ear dips, falters forward . . . Then,
Cross as switches, she's a great horned owl;
Two leafy tricornered ears reverse, a frown
Darkens her chalky visage, big eyes round
And round and stare down midnight.
                                        There sits my cat
Mysterious as gauze,—now somnolent,
Now jocose, quicksilver from a dropped
Thermometer. When poised
Below the sketched ballet-
Dancers who pirouette upon the wall,
Calmly she lifts the slim
Boom of her leg, what will
The prima ballerina next
Perform?—Grace held in readiness,
She meditates, a vision of repose.

BARBARA HOWES

Milk for the Cat

When the tea is brought at five o'clock,
And all the neat curtains are drawn with care,
The little black cat with bright green eyes
Is suddenly purring there.

At first she pretends, having nothing to do,
She has come in merely to blink by the grate,
But, though tea may be late or the milk may be sour,
She is never late.

And presently her agate eyes
Take a soft large milky haze,

And her independent casual glance
Becomes a stiff hard gaze.

Then she stamps her claws or lifts her ears,
Or twists her tail and begins to stir,
Till suddenly all her lithe body becomes
One breathing trembling purr.

The children eat and wriggle and laugh;
The two old ladies stroke their silk:
But the cat is grown small and thin with desire,
Transformed to a creeping lust for milk.

The white saucer like some full moon descends
At last from the clouds of the table above;
She sighs and dreams and thrills and glows,
Transfigured with love.

She nestles over the shining rim,
Buries her chin in the creamy sea;
Her tail hangs loose; each drowsy paw
Is doubled under each bending knee.

A long dim ecstasy holds her life;
Her world is an infinite shapeless white,
Till her tongue has curled the last holy drop,
Then she sinks back into the night,

Draws and dips her body to heap
Her sleepy nerves in the great arm-chair,
Lies defeated and buried deep
Three or four hours unconscious there.

HAROLD MONRO

To a Cat

There is no reason I can find
That you should make me feel so small;
I have a fair to middling mind
While you have almost none at all.
No proud position do you fill;
Your features are extremely plain
And yet I wilt beneath your chill
Disdain.

At night I lie back in my chair
From all my work and worry free
And then I see that sneering stare
Which, from the hearth, you fix on me.
I know I should not strive to please
A dull, unprepossessing cat
But I'm distrait and ill at ease
At that.

You have no power to decide
What I have done or left undone,
You're totally unqualified
For criticising anyone.

I cannot tell why I should fret
At contumely and scorn from you
A mere abysmal brute, and yet
I do.

Some day when in those half closed eyes
I see that sinister regard,
To your annoyance and surprise
You'll land out yonder in the yard.
For praise or place I little care,
From hope of fame I'm quite exempt,
But listen, cat! I cannot bear
Contempt.

ANONYMOUS

Horses and Donkeys

The Horse

I will not change my horse with any that treads . . .
When I bestride him, I soar, I am a hawk.
He trots the air; the earth sings when he touches it.
The basest horn of his hoof is more musical than the pipe of
  Hermes . . .
He's of the color of the nutmeg and of the heat of the ginger . . .
He is pure air and fire, and the dull elements
Of earth and water never appear in him,
But only in patient stillness while his rider mounts him . . .
It is the prince of palfreys. His neigh is like
The bidding of a monarch, and his countenance
Enforces homage.

WILLIAM SHAKESPEARE
(from KING HENRY V, Act 3, Scene 7)

The Runaway

Once, when the snow of the year was beginning to fall,
We stopped by a mountain pasture to say "Whose colt?"
A little Morgan had one forefoot on the wall,
The other curled at his breast. He dipped his head
And snorted to us. And then he had to bolt.
We heard the miniature thunder where he fled

And we saw him or thought we saw him dim and gray,
Like a shadow against the curtain of falling flakes.
"I think the little fellow's afraid of the snow.
He isn't winter-broken. It isn't play
With the little fellow at all. He's running away.
I doubt if even his mother could tell him, 'Sakes,
It's only weather.' He'd think she didn't know.
Where is his mother? He can't be out alone."
And now he comes again with a clatter of stone
And mounts the wall again with whited eyes
And all his tail that isn't hair up straight.
He shudders his coat as if to throw off flies.
"Whoever it is that leaves him out so late,
When other creatures have gone to stall and bin,
Ought to be told to come and take him in."

ROBERT FROST

Mule Song

Oh, the Brown Missouri Mule has a copper-plated throat
And the welkin splits apart when he hits an upper note;
He can warble sweet and low, but he doesn't as a rule,
For there never was a singer like the Brown Missouri Mule.

Oh, the Brown Missouri Mule he can eat a ton of hay,
But he'll pull the biggest load on the hottest summer day
For the shadow of his ears keeps him always fresh and cool;
Oh, there never was a hauler like the Brown Missouri Mule!

Oh, the Brown Missouri Mule he is gentle and refined;
Though he's safe enough in front he is dangerous behind;
There is lightning in his heels so you'd better never fool
With a double-action kicker like the Brown Missouri Mule!

ARTHUR GUITERMAN

Foal

Come trotting up
Beside your mother,
Little skinny.

Lay your neck across
Her back, and whinny,
Little foal.

You think you're a horse
Because you can trot—
But you're not.

Your eyes are so wild,
And each leg is as tall
As a pole;

And you're only a skittish
Child, after all,
Little foal.

MARY BRITTON MILLER

Horse

His bridle hung around the post;
The sun and the leaves made spots come down;
I looked close at him through the fence;
The post was drab and he was brown.

His nose was long and hard and still,
And on his lip were specks like chalk.

But once he opened up his eyes,
And he began to talk.

He didn't talk out with his mouth;
He didn't talk with words or noise.
The talk was there along his nose;
It seemed and then it was.

He said the day was hot and slow,
And he said he didn't like the flies;
They made him have to shake his skin,
And they got drowned in his eyes.

He said that drab was just about
The same as brown, but he was not
A post, he said, to hold a fence.
"I'm horse," he said, "that's what!"

And then he shut his eyes again.
As still as they had been before.
He said for me to run along
And not to bother him any more.

ELIZABETH MADOX ROBERTS

The Broncho That Would Not Be Broken

A little colt—broncho, loaned to the farm
To be broken in time without fury or harm,
Yet black crows flew past you, shouting alarm,
Calling "Beware," with lugubrious singing . . .
The butterflies there in the bush were romancing,
The smell of the grass caught your soul in a trance,
So why be a-fearing the spurs and the traces,
O broncho that would not be broken of dancing?

You were born with the pride of the lords great and olden
Who danced, through the ages, in corridors golden.
In all the wide farm-place the person most human.
You spoke out so plainly with squealing and capering,
With whinnying, snorting contorting and prancing,
As you dodged your pursuers, looking askance,
With Greek-footed figures, and Parthenon paces,
O broncho that would not be broken of dancing.

The grasshoppers cheered. "Keep whirling," they said.
The insolent sparrows called from the shed
"If men will not laugh, make them wish they were dead."
But arch were your thoughts, all malice displacing,
Though the horse-killers came, with snake-whips advancing.
You bantered and cantered away your last chance.
And they scourged you, with Hell in their speech and their faces.
O broncho that would not be broken of dancing.

"Nobody cares for you," rattled the crows,
As you dragged the whole reaper, next day, down the rows.
The three mules held back, yet you danced on your toes.
You pulled like a racer, and kept the mules chasing.
You tangled the harness with bright eyes side-glancing,

While the drunk driver bled you—a pole for a lance—
And the giant mules bit at you—keeping their places,
O broncho that would not be broken of dancing.

In that last afternoon your boyish heart broke.
The hot wind came down like a sledge-hammer stroke.
The blood-sucking flies to a rare feast awoke.
And they searched out your wounds, your death-warrant tracing.
And the merciful men, their religion enhancing,
Stopped the red reaper, to give you a chance.
Then you died on the prairie, and scorned all disgraces,
O broncho that would not be broken of dancing.

VACHEL LINDSAY

Prayer to Go to Paradise with the Donkeys

When You elect to call me, God, O call
When dusty roads proclaim a festival.
As here below I have been wont to do,
I'd like to choose my road to Heaven too,
Where, though we see them not, stars shine by day.
I'll take my stick and tramp the great highway
And to my friends the asses I shall say
"I'm Francis Jammes, and 'tis to Heaven I plod,
For hell's unknown to them that dwell with God.
Come, dear and gentle lovers of blue skies,
Poor beasts who flick your ears to drive away
The blows, the buzzing bees and plaguing flies . . ."

Let me appear among those beasts because
I love them and they droop their heads and pause
And join their little feet so gently that
The heart is filled with pity at their lot.

I'll come escorted by a million ears,
By them that bear big baskets to the marts,
That drag the showmen's caravans and carts
With feather-whisks and tins and kitchen-wares,
By them with battered cans upon their backs,
And lame she-asses full as water-jacks,
By them in little breeches clad because
Their tortured legs are running with blue sores
Besieged by rings of stubborn sucking flies.
With them, God, let me enter Paradise.
Then let the angels tranquilly assemble
And show us bush-grown streams where cherries tremble,
Smooth as the laughing flesh of little maids,
And 'mong the spirits gathered in Your glades
Let me be like Your beasts that bend above
The heavenly waters, where their poverty
Will be reflected everlastingly,
Suffused in Your divine and limpid love.

FRANCIS JAMMES
(Translated from the French by ALAN CONDER)

from *Song of Myself*

A gigantic beauty of a stallion, fresh and responsive to my
caresses.
Head high in the forehead, wide between the ears,
Limbs glossy and supple, tail dusting the ground,
Eyes full of sparkling wickedness, ears finely cut, flexibly moving.
His nostrils dilate as my heels embrace him,
His well-built limbs tremble with pleasure as we race around and
return.

WALT WHITMAN

Nicholas Nye

Thistle and darnel and dock grew there,
   And a bush, in the corner, of may;
On the orchard wall I used to sprawl
   In the blazing heat of the day:
Half asleep and half awake,
   While the birds went twittering by,
And nobody there my lone to share
      But Nicholas Nye.

Nicholas Nye was lean and grey,
   Lame of a leg and old,
More than a score of donkey's years
   He had seen since he was foaled;
He munched the thistles, purple and spiked,
   Would sometimes stoop and sigh,
And turn his head, as if he said,
      "Poor Nicholas Nye!"

Alone with his shadow he'd drowse in the meadow,
   Lazily swinging his tail;
At break of day he used to bray—
   Not much too hearty and hale.
But a wonderful gumption was under his skin,
   And a clear calm light in his eye;
And once in a while: he'd smile a smile,
      Would Nicholas Nye.

Seem to be smiling at me, he would,
   From his bush, in the corner, of may—
Bony and ownerless, widowed and worn,
   Knobble-kneed, lonely, and grey;
And over the grass would seem to pass,
   'Neath the deep dark blue of the sky,

Something much better than words between me
      And Nicholas Nye.

But dusk would come in the apple boughs,
   The green of the glow-worm shine,
The birds in nest would crouch to rest,
   And home I'd trudge to mine;
And there, in the moonlight, dark with dew,
   Asking not wherefore nor why,
Would brood like a ghost, and as still as a post,
      Old Nicholas Nye.

WALTER DE LA MARE

The Four Horses

White Rose is a quiet horse
   For a lady to ride,
Jog-trotting on the high road
   Or through the countryside.

Grey Wolf is a hunter
   All muscle and fire;
Day long he will gallop
   And not tumble or tire.

Black Magic's a race-horse;
   She is gone like a ghost,
With the wind in her mane
   To whirl past the post.

But munching his fill
   In a field of green clover
Stands Brownie the cart-horse,
   Whose labor is over.

JAMES REEVES

Orchard

The mare roamed soft about the slope,
Her rump was like a dancing girl's.
Gentle beneath the apple trees
She pulled the grass and shook the flies.
Her forelocks hung in tawny curls;
She had a woman's limpid eyes,
A woman's patient stare that grieves.
And when she moved among the trees,
The dappled trees, her look was shy,
She hid her nakedness in leaves.
A delicate though weighted dance
She stepped while flocks of finches flew
From tree to tree and shot the leaves
With songs of golden twittering;
How admirable her tender stance.
And then the apple trees were new,
And she was new, and we were new,
And in the barns the stallions stamped
And shook the hills with trumpeting.

RUTH STONE

•

The Ponies

During the strike, the ponies were brought up
From their snug stables, some three hundred feet
Below the surface—up the pit's main shaft
Shot one by one into the light of day;
And as each stepped, bewildered, from the cage,
He stood among his fellows, shivering

In the unaccustomed freshness of free air,
His dim eyes dazzled by the April light.
And then one suddenly left the huddled group,
Lifted his muzzle, sniffed the freshness in,
Pawed the soft turf and, whinneying, started trotting
Across the field; and one by one his fellows
With pricking ears each slowly followed him,
Timidly trotting: when the leader's trot
Broke into a canter, then into a gallop;
And now the whole herd galloped at his heels
Around the dewy meadow, hard hoofs, used
to stumbling over treacherous stony tramways
And plunging hock-deep through black steamy puddles
Of the dusky narrow galleries, delighting
In the soft spring of the resilient turf.
Still round and round the field they raced, unchecked
By tugging traces, at their heels no longer
The trundling tubs, and round and round and round,
With a soft thunder of hoofs, the sunshine flashing
On their sleek coats, through the bright April weather
They raced all day; and even when the night
Kindled clear stars above them in a sky
Strangely unsullied by the stack which now
No longer belched out blackness, still they raced,
Unwearied, as through their short sturdy limbs
The rebel blood like wildfire ran, their lungs
Filled with the breath of freedom. On they sped
Through the sweet dewy darkness; and all night
The watchman at the pithead heard the thudding
Of those careering and exultant hoofs
Still circling in a crazy chase; and dawn
Found them still streaming raggedly around,
Tailing into a lagging cantering,
And so to a stumbling trot: when gradually,
Dropping out one by one, they started cropping
The dew-dank tender grass, which no foul reek

From the long idle pit now smirched, and drinking
With quivering nostrils the rich living breath
Of sappy growing things, the cool rank green
Grateful to eyes, familiar from their colthood
Only with darkness and the dusty glimmer
Of lamplit galleries . . .
Mayhap one day
Our masters, too, will go on strike, and we
Escape the dark and drudgery of the pit,
And race unreined around the fields of heaven!

WILFRID GIBSON

The Donkey

I saw a donkey
  One day old,
His head was too big
  For his neck to hold;
His legs were shaky
  And long and loose,
They rocked and staggered
  And weren't much use.
He tried to gambol
  And frisk a bit,
But he wasn't quite sure
  Of the trick of it.
His queer little coat
  Was soft and grey
And curled at his neck
  In a lovely way.
His face was wistful
  And left no doubt
That he felt life needed

Some thinking out.
So he blundered round
In venturous quest,
And then lay flat
On the ground to rest.
He looked so little
And weak and slim,
I prayed the world
Might be good to him.

GERTRUDE HIND

Dance of Burros

Nothing at all more delicate and charming
than the way the donkeys came,
their eyes downcast like eyes of señoritas
taught to dissemble shame

their small hooves treading neatly, shoes of dancers
making a shape for music, striking the stones
into sudden tune, tapping the brookbed street
to echo on the adobe. How could bones

travel so nimbly under the tall sun
carrying burdens as the donkeys did:
curbed fields of cornstalks? And the pale maize rustled
in frail percussion from the carrying tread.

Piano piano piano the beasts drummed by
with delicate beat, as light as twigs on tile,
through raining light above their own small shadows
trotting in single file.

And three brown men in white, beneath sombreros,
moved with the donkeys quietly, to climb
the cobbled hill. The white walls yawned them in,
burros and men and burdens keeping time.

DILYS LAING

Horse and Hammer

His massive dignity—sixteen
hundred and forty pounds, the poll
of his hemp-hung colossal head
high as the crossbar on the weighing stall,
his half-ton haunches flared
off flanks as limber as steel, great crest
like the hump of a mastodon—
discount. LADIES AND GENTS, YOU HEARD
WHAT THE MAN SAID.
THIS HORSE GOES TO KILL. At best,
the auctioneer drops, momentarily awed,
into intelligibility. SEVENTY-NINE
CENTS ON THE POUND. A fat man
in the ring with a horsewhip
and cigar is making the titan
dance. (A cat couldn't skip
livelier, wince with more exquisite
nerve to the whip's crack.) God
knows he looketh afar off,
who carried for twenty-four years
white clouds and the Catskills on his back,
who wheeled in the width of a turned clod,
or, winters, warmed up a Dutchman's barn
with the steady furnace of his heart . . .
At one hundred twenty-five, he's gone

to the fat horse butcher. Gone
to the dogs; to glue, his hoofs and ears
who could have carried Charlemagne
to the Elbe with all his armor on.

PETER KANE DUFAULT

The Blood Horse

Gamorra is a dainty steed,
Strong, black, and of a noble breed,
Full of fire and full of bone,
With all his line of fathers known;
Fine his nose, his nostrils thin,
But blown abroad by the pride within!
His mane is like a river flowing,
And his eyes like embers glowing
In the darkness of the night,
And his pace as swift as light.

Look,—how round his straining throat
Grace and shifting beauty float;
Sinewy strength is in his reins,
And the red blood gallops through his veins:
Richer, redder, never ran
Through the boasting heart of man.
He can trace his lineage higher
Than the Bourbon dare aspire,—
Douglas, Guzman, or the Guelph,
Or O'Brien's blood itself!

He, who hath no peer, was born
Here, upon a red March morn.
But his famous fathers dead

Were Arabs all, and Arab-bred,
And the last of that great line
Trod like one of a race divine!
And yet,—he was but friend to one
Who fed him at the set of sun
By some lone fountain fringed with green;
With him, a roving Bedouin,
He lived (none else would he obey
Through all the hot Arabian day),
And died untamed upon the sands
Where Balkh amidst the desert stands.

BRYAN W. PROCTER (BARRY CORNWALL)

The War Horse

Then the Lord answered Job out of the whirlwind . . .
Do you give the horse his might?
  Do you clothe his neck with strength?
Do you make him leap like the locust?
  His majestic snorting is terrible.
He paws in the valley, and exults in his strength;
  he goes out to meet the weapons.
He laughs at fear, and is not dismayed;
  he does not turn back from the sword.
Upon him rattle the quiver,
  the flashing spear and the javelin.
With fierceness and rage he swallows the ground;
  he cannot stand still at the sound of the trumpet.
When the trumpet sounds, he says "Aha!"
  He smells the battle from afar,
  the thunder of the captains, and the shouting.

THE BIBLE, REVISED STANDARD VERSION
(from JOB, 39, 19-25)

The Farmyard

Litter of Pigs

On the first cold fall days the little pigs
whine and grumble like bees in a hive.
Nestled in hay they bide their time in a pile,
one on top of the other, a living pyramid.
But the topmost pig, three sides to the cold,
is unsatisfied; he squeals and whines and wiggles,
he works and pushes himself down in the pile,
and another unfortunate forced to the top
squeals and whines and wiggles and pushes in turn.

So they lie until somewhere in the pyramid
one bites the ear of another and bites it hard.
The bitten one squeals as if stuck by a knife.
The pile explodes like a dynamite blast.
The little pigs wheel and run in circles,
they grunt, they whine, they sniff each other,
they grow silent.

The furor over, they return.
The first one snuggles down into the hay;
the next one close beside him, side to side;
another climbs on top; a fourth one pushes in;
and so the living pyramid builds up again,
and one poor pig unfortunate is left on top
and whines and whines and whines.

FRED LAPE

The Pasture

I'm going out to clean the pasture spring;
I'll only stop to rake the leaves away
(And wait to watch the water clear, I may):
I sha'n't be gone long.—You come too.

I'm going out to fetch the little calf
That's standing by the mother. It's so young
It totters when she licks it with her tongue.
I sha'n't be gone long.—You come too.

ROBERT FROST

Fingers in the Nesting Box

My heart would be faithless
If ever I forgot
My farmhouse adventure
One day by the fowl run
When Phoebe (of the fringe
And the fairy-story face)
Incited me to forage
Under speckled feathers
For the first time.

Fabulous I thought it,
Fabulous and fateful
(Before familiarity
With the fond pastime
My feelings blunted),

To clasp in frightened fingers
A firm, warm, round . . .
"Phoebe, dear Phoebe,
What have I found?"

ROBERT GRAVES

Goats

Today I saw, lying in the shade,
Four white goats silhouetted against the grass,
Leaf-shadows lilac across white flanks;
When I came by they were not a bit afraid;
Never a quiver of ears nor a flip of tails;
Only four proud little sculptured heads
Turned slowly in unison to watch me pass.

LYDIA GIBSON

from *Ducks*

When God had finished the stars and whirl of colored suns
He turned His mind from big things to fashion little ones,
Beautiful tiny things (like daisies) He made. and then
He made the comical ones in case the minds of men
  Should stiffen and become
  Dull, humorless and glum:
And so forgetful of their Maker be
As to take even themselves—*quite seriously.*
Caterpillars and cats are lively excellent puns:
All God's jokes are good—even the practical ones!

And as for the duck, I think God must have smiled a bit
Seeing those bright eyes blink on the day He fashioned it.
And He's probably laughing still at the sound that came out of its bill!

F. W. HARVEY

The Ox-Tamer

In a far away northern county in the placid pastoral region,
Lives my farmer friend, the theme of my recitative, a famous tamer of oxen,
There they bring him the three-year-olds and the four-year-olds to break them,
He will take the wildest steer in the world and break him and tame him,
He will go fearless without any whip where the young bullock chafes up and down the yard,
The bullock's head tosses restless high in the air with raging eyes,
Yet see you! how soon his rage subsides—how soon this tamer tames him;
See you! on the farms hereabout a hundred oxen young and old, and he is the man who has tamed them,
They all know him, all are affectionate to him;
See you! some are such beautiful animals, so lofty looking;
Some are buff-coloured, some mottled, one has a white line running along his back, some are brindled,
Some have wide flaring horns (a good sign)—see you! the bright hides,
See, the two with stars on their foreheads—see the round bodies and broad backs,
How straight and square they stand on their legs—what fine sagacious eyes!

How they watch their tamer—they wish him near them—how
they turn to look after him!
What yearning expression! how uneasy they are when he moves
away from them;
Now I marvel what it can be he appears to them (books, politics,
poems, depart—all else departs),
I confess I envy only his fascination—my silent, illiterate friend,
Whom a hundred oxen love there in his life on farms,
In the northern county far, in the placid pastoral region.

WALT WHITMAN

The Lambs of Grasmere, 1860

The upland flocks grew starved and thinned:
Their shepherds scarce could feed the lambs
Whose milkless mothers butted them,
Or who were orphaned of their dams.
The lambs athirst for mother's milk
Filled all the place with piteous sounds:
Their mothers' bones made white for miles
The pastureless wet pasture grounds.

Day after day, night after night,
From lamb to lamb the shepherds went,
With teapots for the bleating mouths,
Instead of nature's nourishment.
The little shivering gaping things
Soon know the step that brought them aid,
And fondled the protecting hand,
And rubbed it with a woolly head.

Then, as the days waxed on to weeks,
It was a pretty sight to see

These lambs with frisky heads and tails
   Skipping and leaping on the lea,
Bleating in tender, trustful tones,
   Resting on rocky crag or mound,
And following the beloved feet
   That once had sought for them and found.

These very shepherds of their flocks,
   These loving lambs so meek to please
Are worthy of recording words
   And honour in their due degrees:
So I might live a hundred years,
   And roam from strand to foreign strand,
Yet not forget this flooded spring
   And scarce-saved lambs of Westmoreland.

CHRISTINA ROSSETTI

The Hens

The night was coming very fast;
It reached the gate as I ran past.

The pigeons had gone to the tower of the church
And all the hens were on their perch,

Up on the barn, and I thought I heard
A piece of a little purring word.

I stopped inside, waiting and staying,
To try to hear what the hens were saying.

They were asking something, that was plain,
Asking it over and over again.

One of them moved and turned around,
Her feathers made a ruffled sound,

A ruffled sound, like a bushful of birds,
And she said her little asking words.

She pushed her head close into her wing,
But nothing answered anything.

ELIZABETH MADOX ROBERTS

The Cow

The cow is of the bovine ilk;
One end is moo, the other, milk.

OGDEN NASH

Sheep Shearing

Poor stubborn sheep, why do you struggle?
Lie still, lie still, and you won't be hurt.
The more you fight the harder to shear you,
the surer I am to nick your skin.
You never learn, your eyes are wild.
You'll fight to the end, and not know why;
only that stronger powers hold you.
You take no chance on their being kind.
And so you struggle and waste your strength.
You twist and the blade slits in your side.
Poor stubborn sheep, lie still, lie still.

FRED LAPE

The Bull Calf

The thing could barely stand. Yet taken
from his mother and the barn smells
he still impressed with his pride,
with the promise of sovereignty in the way
his head moved to take us in.
The fierce sunlight tugging the maize from the ground
licked at his shapely flanks.
He was too young for all that pride.
I thought of the deposed Richard II.
"No money in bull calves," Freeman had said.
The visiting clergyman rubbed the nostrils
now snuffing pathetically at the windless day.
"A pity," he sighed.

My gaze slipped off his hat toward the empty sky
that circled over the black knot of men,
over us and the calf waiting for the first blow.

Struck,
the bull calf drew in his thin forelegs
as if gathering strength for a mad rush . . .
tottered . . . raised his darkening eyes to us,
and I saw we were at the far end
of his frightened look, growing smaller and smaller
till we were only the ponderous mallet
that flicked his bleeding ear
and pushed him over on his side, stiffly,
like a block of wood.

Below the hill's crest
the river snuffled on the improvised beach.
We dug a deep pit and threw the dead calf into it.
It made a wet sound, a sepulchral gurgle,
as the warm sides bulged and flattened.
Settled, the bull calf lay as if asleep,
one foreleg over the other,
bereft of pride and so beautiful now,
without movement, perfectly still in the cool pit,
I turned away and wept.

IRVING LAYTON

Ducks' Ditty

All along the backwater,
Through the rushes tall,
Ducks are a-dabbling,
Up tails all!

Ducks' tails, drakes' tails,
Yellow feet a-quiver,
Yellow bills all out of sight
Busy in the river!

Slushy green undergrowth
Where the roach swim—
Here we keep our larder,
Cool and full and dim.

Everyone for what he likes!
We like to be
Heads down, tails up,
Dabbling free!

High in the blue above
Swifts whirl and call—
We are down a-dabbling
Up tails all!

KENNETH GRAHAME

Moo!

Summer is over, the old cow said,
And they'll shut me up in a draughty shed
To milk me by lamplight in the cold,
But I won't give much for I am old.
It's long ago that I came here
Gay and slim as a woodland deer;
It's long ago that I heard the roar
Of Smith's white bull by the sycamore.
And now there are bones where my flesh should be;
My backbone sags like an old roof tree,

And an apple snatched in a moment's frolic
Is just so many days of colic.
I'm neither a Jersey nor Holstein now
But only a faded sort of cow.
My calves are veal and I had as lief
That I could lay me down as beef;
Somehow, they always kill by halves,—
Why not take me when they take my calves?
Birch turns yellow and sumac red,
I've seen this all before, she said,
I'm tired of the field and tired of the shed.
There's no more grass, there's no more clover;
Summer is over, summer is over.

ROBERT HILLYER

Nosegay for a Young Goat

With what smug elegance the small goat minces
   Over the rocks to me; inquisitive,
Yet quite sedate, he fearlessly evinces
   Interest in what my outstretched hand may give.

His horns are dainty curves, his beard points trimly;
   He has an eye that's both demure and shrewd.
And yet for all he moves his lips so primly,
   Spoken aloud, his language might be lewd.

It makes me smile to see so much that's charming,
   So grave, naïve, and innocent a grace,
An air so decorous and so disarming,
   Combined with that uncouth and crafty face.

WINIFRED WELLES

Rooster

His feathers are burnished gold;
On tiptoes he crows debonair;
He claws up roots in the garden
And sorts his booty with care.

A worthy paterfamilias,
He surveys his chicks with a tingle
Of pride; struts the yard like a warrior—
A pity his spurs never jingle!

His life is battles and flights;
Like an eagle he'll dart and be gone;
He fights with the neighbor's cock
Day long until blood is drawn.

He pulls his frayed cloak close,
Deep in thought on the perch; he thrives
Like the Mongols of old; a hundred
Fights, and a score of wives.

FYODOR BELKIN
(Translated from the Russian by BABETTE DEUTSCH)

Pearls Among Swine

"Yes, there's nothing cuter in all this world
Than a little ole baby pig,"
Said my wiley country cousin, grinning big
As he reached down and plucked one like an intricate plum
From its milk-swollen udder on the sow

And sent it squealing on elfin hooves
To another fat twig on that great, bloated bough,
And I agreed with him: it was dainty in every feature,
An exquisite silk purse born of a gross and slovenly creature
As of a monstrous oyster pearled . . .

PEGGY BENNETT

April

The little goat
crops
new grass lying down
leaps up eight inches
into air and
lands on four feet.
Not a tremor—
solid in the
spring and serious
he walks away.

YVOR WINTERS

The Lamb

Little Lamb, who made thee?
Dost thou know who made thee?
Gave thee life, and bid thee feed,
By the stream and o'er the mead;
Gave thee clothing of delight,
Softest clothing, woolly, bright;
Gave thee such a tender voice,

Making all the vales rejoice?
  Little Lamb, who made thee?
  Dost thou know who made thee?

  Little Lamb, I'll tell thee,
  Little Lamb, I'll tell thee:
  He is called by thy name,
For He calls Himself a Lamb.
He is meek, and He is mild;
He became a little child.
I a child, and thou a lamb,
We are called by His name.
  Little Lamb, God bless thee!
  Little Lamb, God bless thee!

WILLIAM BLAKE

A Child's Pet

When I sailed out of Baltimore,
  With twice a thousand head of sheep,
They would not eat, they would not drink,
  But bleated o'er the deep.

Inside the pens we crawled each day,
  To sort the living from the dead;
And when we reached the Mersey's mouth,
  Had lost five hundred head.

Yet every night and day one sheep,
  That had no fear of man or sea,
Stuck through the bars its pleading face,
  And it was stroked by me.

And to the sheep-men standing near,
"You see," I said, "this one tame sheep?
It seems a child has lost her pet,
And cried herself to sleep."

So every time we passed it by,
Sailing to England's slaughter-house,
Eight ragged sheep-men—tramps and thieves—
Would stroke that sheep's black nose.

W. H. DAVIES

Cows

Half the time they munched the grass, and all the time they lay
Down in the water-meadows, the lazy month of May,
A-chewing,
A-mooing,
To pass the hours away.

"Nice weather," said the brown cow.
"Ah," said the white.
"Grass is very tasty."
"Grass is all right."

Half the time they munched the grass, and all the time they lay
Down in the water-meadows, the lazy month of May,
A-chewing,
A-mooing,
To pass the hours away.

"Rain coming," said the brown cow.
"Ah," said the white.

"Flies is very tiresome."
"Flies bite."

Half the time they munched the grass, and all the time they lay
Down in the water-meadows, the lazy month of May,
A-chewing,
A-mooing,
To pass the hours away.

"Time to go," said the brown cow.
"Ah," said the white.
"Nice chat." "Very pleasant."
"Night." "Night."

Half the time they munched the grass, and all the time they lay
Down in the water-meadows, the lazy month of May,
A-chewing,
A-mooing,
To pass the hours away.

JAMES REEVES

Country Idyll

Deep in the stable tied with rope,
The cow has neither dignity nor hope.

With ugly, puzzled, hot despair
She needs the calf that is not there,
And mourns and mourns him to unheeding air.

But if the sleeping farmer hears,
He pulls the blanket higher round his ears.

FRANCES CORNFORD

from *Farm Yard at Evening*

. . . Round the yard, a thousand ways
Beasts in expectation gaze,
Catching at the loads of hay
Passing fodders tug away.
Hogs with grumbling, deafening voice
Bother round the server boys;
And, far and near, the motley group
Anxious claim their suppering-up.
From the rest, a blest release,
Gabbling home, the quarreling geese
Seek their warm, straw-littered shed
And, waddling, prate away to bed.

Nighted* by unseen delay,
Poking hens, that lose their way
On the hovel's rafters rise,
Slumbering there, the fox's prize.
Now the cat has ta'en her seat
With her tail curled round her feet;

* nighted: surrounded by darkness

Patiently she sits to watch
Sparrows fighting on the thatch.
Now Doll brings the expected pails,
And dogs begin to wag their tails;
With strokes and pats they're welcomed in,
And they with looking wants begin;
Slove* in the milk-pail brimming o'er,
She pops their dish behind the door.

JOHN CLARE

Quack!

The duck is whiter than whey is,
His tail tips up over his back,
The eye in his head is as round as a button,
And he says, *Quack! Quack!*

He swims on his bright blue mill-pond,
By the willow-tree under the shack,
Then stands on his head to see down to the bottom,
And says, *Quack! Quack!*

When Molly steps out of the kitchen,
For apron—pinned round with a sack;
He squints at her round face, her dish, and what's in it,
And says, *Quack! Quack!*

He preens the pure snow of his feathers
In the sun by the wheat-straw stack;
At dusk waddles home with his brothers and sisters,
And says, *Quack! Quack!*

WALTER DE LA MARE

* slove: slily

Biddy

And not one word for Biddy, the placid one,
a word of praise for Biddy, the average hen?
She is not wise nor proud nor beautiful.
She eats, she sings, she scratches for dirt;
she dusts herself, she lays an egg in a box;
she sleeps at night with her head under her wing.

Say she is stupid, her brain is little.
What fault is that of hers? She is as she was hatched.
Nothing that she can do will change her.
She and her millions of sisters cover the earth.
They cackle and lay their eggs, and keep well fed
the gullets of millions of mortals.

FRED LAPE

Impasse

Six little sheep
Bleating in the sun,
Don't know which
Way they should run.

Fence to the left;
Fence to the right;
Before them a mouse
Stabs them with fright.

Nothing to do
But to wheel and go—
A little too much
For sheep to know.

LEW SARETT

Big Beasts, Wild Beasts

Lion

The lion, ruler over all the beasts,
Triumphant moves upon the grassy plain
With sun like gold upon his tawny brow
And dew like silver on his shaggy mane.

Into himself he draws the rolling thunder,
Beneath his flinty paw great boulders quake;
He will dispatch the mouse to burrow under,
The little deer to shiver in the brake.

He sets the fierce whip of each serpent lashing,
The tall giraffe brings humbly to his knees,
Awakes the sloth, and sends the wild boar crashing,
Wide-eyed monkeys chittering, through the trees.

He gazes down into the quiet river,
Parting the green bulrushes to behold
A sunflower-crown of amethyst and silver,
A royal coat of brushed and beaten gold.

WILLIAM JAY SMITH

Greed

The Hyena trembled
Like a glitter of glass;

Violently shivering
He paced the cage,

Growing ever more agitated
Until it was

With a leap to the east
And a leap to the west

Varied by a rapid slinking
Around the walls

He danced his agony
of hunger.

The keeper came with a tray
Of red raw meat.

The Hyena shook so pitifully
He could scarcely eat,

But gobbled it in a trice.
If one looked twice

Before the keeper had passed on,
The meat was all gone,

There being no meal so nourishing
It can assuage

The ravenings of so insatiably
Ambitious a beast;

He eats for future famines
Who nurses never-ending rage—

Devours all posterity
And dies hungry.

PEGGY BENNETT

The Giraffe

Hide of a leopard and hide of a deer
And eyes of a baby calf,
Sombre and large and crystal clear,
And a comical back that is almost sheer
Has the absurd giraffe.

A crane all covered with hide and hair
Is the aslant giraffe,
So cleverly mottled with many a square
That even the jungle is unaware
Whether a pair or a herd are there,
Or possibly one giraffe,
Or possibly only half.

If you saw him stoop and straddle and drink
He would certainly make you laugh,
He would certainly make you laugh, I think
With his head right down on the water's brink,
Would the invert giraffe,
The comical knock-kneed, angular, crock-kneed,
Anyhow-built giraffe.

There's more than a grain of common sense
And a husky lot of chaff
In the many and various arguments
About the first giraffe,
The first and worst giraffe;
Whether he grows a neck because
He yearned for the higher shoots
Out of the reach of all and each
Of the ruminating brutes;
Or whether he got to the shoots because
His neck was long, if long it was,
Is the cause of many disputes
Over the ladder without any rungs,
The stopper-like mouth and the longest of tongues
Of the rum and dumb giraffe,
The how-did-you-come giraffe,
The brown equatorial, semi-arboreal
Head-in-the-air giraffe.

GEOFFREY DEARMER

Baby Camel

Leaning against the long legs of a camel
Stands, not a baby camel, but a marvel.

He has not lived more than a little while—
This yellow hump on downy matchstick legs.

He has not lived more than an hour perhaps,
Yet he can yell, and in a haughty bass.

What dignity is in the little head
That reaches out toward the *saksaul** twigs.

* saksaul: small leafless tree growing in the deserts of Central Asia

The nose is a black patch that, twitching, sniffs
The thick sweet smell, the homely smell of milk.

He totters off. If he walks clumsily,
In every movement there is camel pride,

Declaring: I will be a richer yellow,
Carry a grander hump than all my brothers.

VADIM KOROSTYLEV
(Translated from the Russian by BABETTE DEUTSCH)

Blacktail Deer

The blacktail held his tawny marble pose,
With every supple muscle set to spring,
Nosing the tainted air—his slender limbs
And sinews like corded copper quivering.

Ponderous the minutes, while his smouldering eyes
Went burning over me, and searching mine;
His heart ticked off each moment as he stood
Waiting an ominous word, a sound, a sign.

I tossed a friendly gesture! The sinews snapped
And flung his bulk of rippled tawny stone
Over an alder, as when a bended pine,
Released from pressure, catapults a cone.

Bending an arch above the alder-crown,
In a stream of whistling wind the great buck went,
Flirting his tail in exclamation-marks
To punctuate his vast astonishment.

LEW SARETT

A Story for a Child

Little one, come to my knee!
  Hark, how the rain is pouring
Over the roof, in the pitch-black night,
  And the wind in the woods a-roaring!

Hush, my darling, and listen,
  Then pay for the story with kisses;
Father was lost in the pitch-black night,
  In just such a storm as this is!

High up on the lonely mountains,
  Where the wild men watched and waited;
Wolves in the forest, and bears in the bush,
  And I on my path belated.

The rain and the night together
  Came down, and the wind came after,
Bending the props of the pine-tree roof,
  And snapping many a rafter.

I crept along in the darkness,
  Stunned, and bruised, and blinded,—
Crept to a fir with thick-set boughs,
  And a sheltering rock behind it.

There, from the blowing and raining,
  Crouching, I sought to hide me:
Something rustled, two green eyes shone,
  And a wolf lay down beside me.

Little one, be not frightened;
  I and the wolf together,

Side by side, through the long, long night
  Hid from the awful weather.

His wet fur pressed against me;
  Each of us warmed the other;
Each of us felt, in the stormy dark,
  That beast and man were brother.

And when the falling forest
  No longer crashed in warning,
Each of us went from our hiding place
  Forth in the wild, wet morning.

Darling, kiss me in payment!
  Hark, how the wind is roaring;
Father's house is a better place
  When the stormy rain is pouring!

BAYARD TAYLOR

Rose's Calf

The hippopotamus has calved beside her pool
A calf sublime,
But, alas, born in technicolor,
A bright raw pink.
However, the attendants reassure us,
It will darken with time,
Brown—like the petals of an exhausted rose.

Meanwhile the chubby infant dives underwater to nurse,
While its huge mother, reclining on her side
With her short legs sticking out like little stumps,
Resembles an overturned bed

Dumped where an incoming tide
Partially surrounds it, lapping its bulging upholstery,
Pillows, billowing through.

Between its heady sucks and swallows
At the drowned font of maternal ale,
The newborn raises its flaring pug nostrils
From the water to suck the air.
It is truly amphibious. Therefore, unlike a whale,
Presently it will stand on dry land, four-legged, four-square,
Stubborn as a little mule.

PEGGY BENNETT

The Fawn

There it was I saw what I shall never forget
And never retrieve.
Monstrous and beautiful to human eyes, hard to believe,
He lay, yet there he lay,
Asleep on the moss, his head on his polished cleft small ebony
hooves,
The child of the doe, the dappled child of the deer.

Surely his mother had never said, "Lie here
Till I return," so spotty and plain to see
On the green moss lay he.
His eyes had opened; he considered me.

I would have given more than I care to say
To thrifty ears, might I have had him for my friend
One moment only of that forest day:

Might I have had the acceptance, not the love
Of those clear eyes;

Might I have been for him the bough above
Or the root beneath his forest bed,
A part of the forest, seen without surprise.
Was it alarm, or was it the wind of my fear lest he depart
That jerked him to his jointy knees,
And sent him crashing off, leaping and stumbling
On his new legs, between the stems of the white trees?

EDNA ST. VINCENT MILLAY

The Panther

The panther is like a leopard,
Except it hasn't been peppered.
Should you behold a panther crouch,
Prepare to say Ouch.
Better yet, if called by a panther,
Don't anther.

OGDEN NASH

Lord of Jesters, Prince of Fellows

Chimpanzee, you have kindly eyes
Like tiny brown berries, juicy, wise,
So reminiscent of the mandarin Chinese
Who never squatted on the limbs of trees.

Chimpanzee, whose round eyes peer
Through the keyhole of an ancient joke,
Who rides a bicycle, carries a parasol,
And begs a cigar to smoke,

Chimpanzee, at home anywhere, everywhere,
Garbed like dapper dan, or in livery like a flunkey,
Charming, humorous, congenial, and debonair,
You are the wit absent in the Gorilla and the Monkey.

PEGGY BENNETT

The Zebras

From the dark woods that breathe of fallen showers,
Harnessed with level rays in golden reins,
The zebras draw the dawn across the plains
Wading knee-deep among the scarlet flowers.
The sunlight, zithering their flanks with fire,
Flashes between the shadows as they pass
Barred with electric tremors through the grass
Like wind along the golden strings of a lyre.
Into the flushed air snorting rosy plumes
That smolder round their feet in drifting fumes,
With dove-like voices call the distant fillies,
While round the herds the stallion wheels his flight,
Engine of beauty volted with delight,
To roll his mare among the trampled lilies.

ROY CAMPBELL

The Sloth

In moving-slow he has no Peer.
You ask him something in his ear;
He thinks about it for a Year.

And then, before he says a Word
There, upside down (unlike a Bird)
He will assume that you have Heard—

A most Ex-as-per-at-ing Lug.
But should you call his manner Smug,
He'll sigh and give his Branch a Hug;

Then off again to Sleep he goes,
Still swaying gently by his Toes,
And you just know he *knows* he knows.

THEODORE ROETHKE

Are You a Marsupial?

Now are you a marsupial?
And have you a little pouch?
If I pinch it on the outside
Does something inside holler "Ouch!"?

No.

JOHN BECKER

The Rhinoceros

I love to wallow in the mud
  That borders on the stream;
I love to lie and cool my blood
  And meditate and dream

Wrinkled and horny is my flesh,
Angry my eye and wild,
And yet my soul is smooth and fresh
Like that of any child.

Man looks upon me with a frown
And holds me as a foe;
And yet I only knock him down
Because I love him so.

Many a human I have hurled
To earth, and trampled flat;
And is there, friends, in all the world
A purer love than that?

R. P. LISTER

Plain Talk for a Pachyderm

Spruce up, O Baggy Elephant!
Firm and conform that globular figger,
For, although you yourself may think you've outgrown your britches,
Either you've lost weight or your coveralls have stretched:
They appear to be a whole mountain size bigger.

Now, this isn't Skid Row on the Bowery, you know!
You could use a lot more starch in your clothes,
Iron out maybe a billion wrinkles before the next opening of the gates,
And tuck up that dangling nose
Which snuffles around your ankles like an old loose stocking that got lost from a foot.

You never can tell just who might show up out here, you know,

You sloppy pachyderm!
You don't want people whispering amongst themselves,
"Hey, get a load of this big bum!"

PEGGY BENNETT

A Runnable Stag

When the pods went pop on the broom, green broom,
  And apples began to be golden-skinn'd,
We harbour'd a stag in the Priory coomb,
  And we feather'd his trail up-wind, up-wind,
  We feather'd his trail up-wind—
    A stag of warrant, a stag, a stag,
    A runnable stag, a kingly crop,
    Brow, bay and tray and three on top,
    A stag, a runnable stag.

Then the huntsman's horn rang yap, yap, yap,
  And "Forwards" we heard the harbourer shout;
But 'twas only a brocket that broke a gap
  In the beechen underwood, driven out,
  From the underwood antler'd out
    By warrant and might of the stag, the stag,
    The runnable stag, whose lordly mind
    Was bent on sleep, though beam'd and tined
    He stood, a runnable stag.

So we tufted the covert till afternoon
  With Tinkerman's Pup and Bell-of-the-North;
And hunters were sulky and hounds out of tune
  Before we tufted the right stag forth,
  Before we tufted him forth,
    The stag of warrant, the wily stag,

The runnable stag with his kingly crop,
Brow, bay and tray and three on top,
The royal and runnable stag.

It was Bell-of-the-North and Tinkerman's Pup
That stuck to the scent till the copse was drawn.
"Tally ho! tally ho!" and the hunt was up,
The tufters whipp'd and the pack laid on,
The resolute pack laid on,
And the stag of warrant away at last,
The runnable stag, the same, the same,
His hoofs on fire, his horns like flame,
A stag, a runnable stag.

"Let your gelding be: if you check or chide
He stumbles at once and you're out of the hunt;
For three hundred gentlemen, able to ride,
On hunters accustom'd to bear the brunt,
Accustom'd to bear the brunt,
Are after the runnable stag, the stag,
The runnable stag with his kingly crop,
Brow, bay and tray and three on top,
The right, the runnable stag."

By perilous paths in coomb and dell,
The heather, the rocks, and the river-bed,
The pace grew hot, for the scent lay well,
And a runnable stag goes right ahead,
The quarry went right ahead—
Ahead, ahead, and fast and far;
His antler'd crest, his cloven hoof,
Brown, bay and tray and three aloof,
The stag, the runnable stag.

For a matter of twenty miles and more,
By the densest hedge and the highest wall,

Through herds of bullocks he baffled the lore
Of harbourer, huntsman, hounds and all,
Of harbourer, hounds and all—
The stag of warrant, the wily stag,
For twenty miles, and five and five,
He ran, and he never was caught alive,
This stag, this runnable stag.

When he turn'd at bay in the leafy gloom,
In the emerald gloom where the brook ran deep
He heard in the distance the rollers boom,
And he saw in a vision of peaceful sleep,
A stag of warrant, a stag, a stag,
A runnable stag in a jewell'd bed,
Under the sheltering ocean dead,
A stag, a runnable stag.

So a fateful hope lit up his eye,
And he open'd his nostrils wide again,
And he toss'd his branching antlers high
As he headed the hunt down the Charlock glen
As he raced down the echoing glen—
For five miles more, the stag, the stag,
For twenty miles, and five and five,
Not to be caught now, dead or alive,
The stag, the runnable stag,

Three hundred gentlemen, able to ride,
Three hundred horses as gallant and free,
Beheld him escape on the evening tide,
Far out till he sank in the Severn Sea,
Till he sank in the depths of the sea—
The stag, the buoyant stag, the stag
That slept at last in a jewell'd bed
Under the sheltering ocean spread,
The stag, the runnable stag.

JOHN DAVIDSON

The Captive Lion

Thou that in fury with thy knotted tail
Hast made this iron floor thy beaten drum;
That now in silence walks thy little space—
Like a sea-captain—careless what may come:

What power has brought your majesty to this,
Who gave those eyes their dull and sleepy look;
Who took their lightning out, and from thy throat
The thunder when the whole wide forest shook?

It was that man who went again, alone,
Into thy forest dark—Lord, he was brave!
That man a fly has killed, whose bones are left
Unburied till an earthquake digs his grave.

W. H. DAVIES

The Flower-fed Buffaloes

The flower-fed buffaloes of the spring
In the days of long ago,
Ranged where the locomotives sing
And the prairie flowers lie low:
The tossing, blooming, perfumed grass
Is swept away by the wheat,
Wheels and wheels and wheels spin by
In the spring that still is sweet.
But the flower-fed buffaloes of the spring
Left us, long ago.

They gore no more, they bellow no more,
They trundle around the hills no more:
With the Blackfeet, lying low,
With the Pawnees, lying low,
Lying low.

VACHEL LINDSAY

Au Jardin Des Plantes

The gorilla lay on his back,
One hand cupped under his head,
Like a man.

Like a laboring man tired with work,
A strong man with his strength burnt away
In the toil of earning a living.

Only of course he was not tired out with work,
Merely with boredom; his terrible strength
All burnt away by prodigal idleness.

A thousand days, and then a thousand days,
Idleness licked away his beautiful strength,
He having no need to earn a living.

It was all laid on, free of charge.
We maintained him, not for doing anything,
But for being what he was.

And so that Sunday morning he lay on his back,
Like a man, like a worn-out man,
One hand cupped under his terrible hard head.

Like a man, like a man,
One of those we maintain, not for doing anything,
But for being what they are.

A thousand days, and then a thousand days,
With everything laid on, free of charge,
They cup their heads in prodigal idleness.

JOHN WAIN

I Had a Hippopotamus

I had a hippopotamus; I kept him in a shed
And fed him upon vitamins and vegetable bread;
I made him my companion on many cheery walks
And had his portrait done by a celebrity in chalks.

His charming eccentricities were known on every side,
The creature's popularity was wonderfully wide;
He frolicked with the Rector in a dozen friendly tussles,
Who could not but remark upon his hippopotamuscles.

If he should be afflicted by depression or the dumps,
By hippopotameasles or the hippopotamumps,
I never knew a particle of peace till it was plain
He was hippopotamasticating properly again.

I had a hippopotamus; I loved him as a friend;
But beautiful relationships are bound to have an end.
Time takes, alas! our joys from us and robs us of our blisses;
My hippopotamus turned out a hippopotamissis.

My housekeeper regarded him with jaundice in her eye;
She did not want a colony of hippopotami;

She borrowed a machine-gun from her soldier-nephew, Percy,
And showed my hippopotamus no hippopotamercy.

My house now lacks the glamour that the charming creature
gave,
The garage where I kept him is as silent as the grave;
No longer he displays among the motor-tires and spanners
His hippopotamastery of hippopotamanners.

No longer now he gambols in the orchard in the Spring
No longer do I lead him through the village on a string;
No longer in the mornings does the neighborhood rejoice
To his hippopotamusically-modulated voice.

I had a hippopotamus; but nothing upon earth
Is constant in its happiness or lasting in its mirth.
No joy that life can give me can be strong enough to smother
My sorrow for that might-have-been-a-hippopotamother.

PATRICK BARRINGTON

Truth Will Out

The Aoudads are horned creatures
Of amiable habits;
They look more like goats than sheep,
Multiply like rabbits,
And adapt themselves philosophically
To life in our animal jails,
Never once reproaching us
With sad looks like mournful tales
Summing up lost splendors
They, or their ancestry, once knew
High in the Atlas mountains

Overlooking the Sahara's orange sand.
Wisely, they seem to accept a view less grand
Of their twisted fate, called kismet—
But now and then they startle spectators in a zoo
By running full tilt at a perpendicular wall
And leaping high upon it with all four feet
Before dropping off like a rebounding ball
Onto their nimble hooves: *It's just as they might do*
High in the Atlas mountains, in their own, their native land.

PEGGY BENNETT

At the Lion's Cage

I have some sympathy for that cat
who paces, paces his pismire-
pavemented dungeon——three short strides,
then blink and turn,
then blink and turn——much marvelled at:
"Mama, how come he walks like that?"

"He wants t'get out, Richie, he sees
d'monkey." But the sign belies
any specified hunger: BORN AND RAISED
IN CAPTIVITY.
Captivity. He walks because
his heart is hunting. Those soft paws,

although they never fell thereon,
measure the breadth of Africa;
that throat and belly are athirst
for blood of bulls,
for blood of bulls; the pale eyes shine
back at the Mountains Of The Moon.

I have some sympathy for one
whose office space is small, at whom
civilization gapes because
he can't keep still,
keep still a body forged and honed
to bring the Mammoth crashing down.

PETER KANE DUFAULT

Monkeys

Two little creatures
With faces the size of
A pair of pennies
Are clasping each other.
"Ah, do not leave me,"
One says to the other,
In the high monkey-
Cage in the beast-shop.

There are no people to gape at them now,
For people are loth to
Peer in the dimness;
Have they not builded
Streets and playhouses,
Sky-signs and bars,
To lose the loneliness
Shaking the hearts
Of the two little Monkeys?

Yes. But who watches
The penny-small faces
Can hear the voices:
"Ah, do not leave me;

Suck I will give you,
Warmth and clasping,
And if you slip from
This beam I can never
Find you again."

Dim is the evening,
And chill is the weather;
There, drawn from their colored
Hemisphere,
The apes lilliputian
With faces the size of
A pair of pennies,
And voices as low as
The flow of my blood.

PADRAIC COLUM

Bird Thou Never Wert

I.

Lo, here the gentle Yak, weary of rest,
Sprays up the dust of his patio with a moist sneeze,
Mounts up on his hind legs from his front knees,
Whence he clambers to his calloused feet.
He is not, nor has he ever been, neat.
His curls are matted; in a wood he would hang
From every bush like an earthbound Absalom,
A fat folded rug, spawned by a heavy awning.

II.

Hark! hark! the Yak at his iron gate snorts
And rolls his cretin eyes.
He wants no truck with Lion or Duck; no key to Paradise
Can shake that earthbound mountain into a dance of glee.

With heavy glower he paws his bower
And slumps downward again in customary lethargy
From which no mere yeast of merriment
Will ever move the sullen beast to rise.

PEGGY BENNETT

Exile

Ben-Arabie was the Camel,
  Belonging to the Zoo.
He lived there through a dozen years,
  With nothing much to do,
But chew, and chew, and chew, and chew,
  And chew, and chew, and chew.

He wondered when he might go home,—
  And what they kept him for;
Because he hated Zooish sounds
  And perfumes—more and more;—
Decidedly he hated them
  Much more, and more, and more.

And why the world turned white and cold
  He did not understand.
He only wanted lots of sun
  And lots and lots of sand;
Just sand, and sand, and sand, and sand,
  And sand, and sand, and sand.

He longed to see an Arab Sheik,
  And Arab girls and boys;
The kind of noise he yearned for most
  Was plain Arabian noise;

(The sound of little drums and flutes
And all that sort of noise.)

He leant against the wind to hear
The sound of harness bells;
He sniffed the air for scent of spice
The nomad merchant sells;
He dreamed of pleasant tinkling bells,
Of spice, and tinkling bells.

The keepers said that he grew queer.
They wondered why he sighed;
They called him supercilious
And crabbed and sun-dried;
(Indeed he was quite crabbed and
Exceedingly sun-dried.)

But ere his woolly fur was gone
They put him on a train—
For a rich old Arab bought him
And sent him home again;—
O joyous day! He sent him home;
He sent him home again!

VIRNA SHEARD

The Boar

On his bow-back he hath a battle set
Of bristly pikes, that ever threat his foes;
His eyes like glow-worms shine when he doth fret;
His snout digs sepulchres where'er he goes;
Being mov'd, he strikes whate'er is in his way
And whom he strikes his crooked tushes slay.

His brawny sides, with hairy bristles arm'd,
Are better proof than thy spear's point can enter;
His short thick neck cannot be easily harm'd;
Being ireful, on the lion he will venture:
The thorny brambles and embracing bushes
As fearful of him part; through whom he rushes.

WILLIAM SHAKESPEARE
(from VENUS AND ADONIS)

Grizzly

Coward,—of heroic size,
In whose lazy muscles lies
Strength we fear and yet despise;
Savage,—whose relentless tusks
Are content with acorn husks;
Robber,—whose exploits ne'er soared
O'er the bee's or squirrel's hoard;
Whiskered chin, and feeble nose,
Claws of steel on baby toes,—
Here, in solitude and shade,
Shambling, shuffling plantigrade,
Be thy courses undismayed!

Here, where Nature makes thy bed,
Let thy rude, half-human tread
   Point to hidden Indian springs,
Lost in ferns and fragrant grasses,
   Hovered o'er by timid wings,
Where the wood-duck lightly passes,
Where the wild bee holds her sweets,
Epicurean retreats,
Fit for thee, and better than
Fearful spoils of dangerous man.
In thy fat-jowled deviltry
Friar Tuck shall live in thee;
Thou mayest levy tithe and dole;
   Thou shalt spread the woodland cheer,
From the pilgrim taking toll;
   Match thy cunning with his fear;
Eat, and drink, and have thy fill;
Yet remain an outlaw still!

BRET HARTE

Deer

Proud in a cloud of sun
Stands deer,
His head held high
As petals fall
Over his quivering flanks.

Under a tree
Brighter than sun
Stands deer
Rubbing moss
From his polished weapons.

HARRY BEHN

A Snap Judgment of the Llama

The Llama seems a sensitive creature,
Quiet and aloof, shy, discreet;
Her neck seems a bit long, as a leg is long,
But she has slender ankles and dainty feet—
And gazes on her present strange fortunes
With many a delicate sniff,
Her quickfingered hare-nose wiggling constantly
As if being nibbled inward by its own self.

PEGGY BENNETT

The Tiger

Tiger! Tiger! burning bright
In the forests of the night,
What immortal hand or eye
Could frame thy fearful symmetry?

In what distant deeps or skies
Burnt the fire of thine eyes?
On what wings dare he aspire?
What the hand dare seize the fire?

And what shoulder, and what art,
Could twist the sinews of thy heart?
And when thy heart began to beat,
What dread hand? and what dread feet?

What the hammer? what the chain?
In what furnace was thy brain?

What the anvil? what dread grasp
Dare its deadly terrors clasp?

When the stars threw down their spears,
And water'd heaven with their tears,
Did he smile his work to see?
Did he who made the Lamb make thee?

Tiger! Tiger! burning bright
In the forests of the night,
What immortal hand or eye,
Dare frame thy fearful symmetry?

WILLIAM BLAKE

from *The Flaming Terrapin*

Out of the Ark's grim hold
A torrent of spendor rolled—
From the hollow resounding sides,
Flashing and glittering, came
Panthers with sparkled hides,
And tigers scribbled with flame,
And lions in grisly trains
Cascading their golden manes.
They ramped in the morning light,
And over their stripes and stars
The sun-shot lightnings, quivering bright,
Rippled in zigzag bars.
The wildebeest frisked with the gale
On the crags of a hunchback mountain,
With his heels in the clouds, he flirted his tail
Like the jet of a silvery fountain.
Frail oribi sailed with their golden-skinned

And feathery limbs laid light on the wind.
And the springbok bounced, and fluttered, and flew,
Hooped their spines on the gaunt karroo.
Gay zebras pranced and snorted aloud—
With the crackle of hail their hard hoofs pelt,
And thunder breaks from the rolling cloud
That they raise on the dusty Veldt.
O, hark how the rapids of the Congo
Are chanting their rolling strains,
And the sun-dappled herds a-skipping to the song, go
Kicking up the dust on the great, grey plains—
Tsessebe, Koodoo, Buffalo, Bongo,
With the fierce wind foaming in their manes.

ROY CAMPBELL

Buzzers, Leapers, and Flyers

The King of Yellow Butterflies

The King of Yellow Butterflies,
The King of Yellow Butterflies,
The King of Yellow Butterflies,
Now orders forth his men.
He says, "The time is almost here
When violets bloom again."
Adown the road the fickle rout
Goes flashing proud and bold
Adown the road the fickle rout
Goes flashing proud and bold,
Adown the road the fickle rout
Goes flashing proud and bold,
They shiver by the shallow pools,
They shiver by the shallow pools,
They shiver by the shallow pools,
And whimper of the cold.
They drink and drink. A frail pretence!
They love to pose and preen.
Each pool is but a looking glass,
Where their sweet wings are seen.
Each pool is but a looking glass,
Where their sweet wings are seen.
Each pool is but a looking glass,
Where their sweet wings are seen.
Gentlemen adventurers! Gypsies every whit!
They live on what they steal. Their wings
By briars are frayed a bit.

Their loves are light. They have no house.
And if it rains today,
They'll climb into your cattle-shed,
They'll climb into your cattle-shed,
They'll climb into your cattle-shed,
And hide them in the hay,
And hide them in the hay,
And hide them in the hay,
And hide them in the hay.

VACHEL LINDSAY

Beetle

A beetle caught my eye, one day,
Beside the path:
There, with his head buried deep in a daisy-centre,
Pigging and bolting it—great, scented, yellow mouthfuls—
With the space he had already eaten
Blackened around him;
There he gorged, standing on his ridiculous, gluttonous head,
With his hard, thin legs
Straight up in the forgotten air,
And his head deep in a dim, succulent heaven.

"So," I thought, "For his belly's sake,
Beauty must go."

But then I looked again, more closely—
The beetle was far lovelier than the flower,
Alone, among a hundred of the daisies—
And so I was content
And left him there.

HUGH FINN

the flattered lightning bug

a lightning bug got
in here the other night a
regular hick from
the real country he was
awful proud of himself you
city insects may think
you are some punkins
but i don t see any
of you flashing in the dark
like we do in
the country all right go
to it says i mehitabel the
cat and that green
spider who lives in your locker
and two or three cockroach
friends of mine and a
friendly rat all gathered
around him and urged him on
and he lightened and
lightened and lightened you
don t see anything like this
in town often he says go to it
we told him it s a
real treat to us and
we nicknamed him broadway
which pleased him
this is the life
he said all i
need is a harbor
under me to be a
statue of liberty and
he got so vain of

himself i had to take
him down a peg you ve
made lightning for two hours
little bug i told him
but i don t hear
any claps of thunder
yet there are some men
like that when he wore
himself out mehitabel
the cat ate him

archy

DON MARQUIS

The Grasshopper and the Cricket

Green little vaulter in the sunny grass,
Catching your heart up at the feel of June,
Sole voice that's heard amidst the lazy noon,
When even the bees lag at the summoning brass;
And you, warm little housekeeper, who class
With those who think the candles come too soon,
Loving the fire, and with your tricksome tune
Nick the glad silent moments as they pass;

Oh sweet and tiny cousins, that belong,
One to the fields, the other to the hearth,
Both have your sunshine; both though small are strong
At your clear hearts; and both seem given to earth
To ring in thoughtful ears this natural song—
Indoors and out, summer and winter, Mirth.

LEIGH HUNT

Honey-Bees

They have a king and officers of sorts;
Where some, like magistrates, correct at home,
Others, like merchants, venture trade abroad,
Others, like soldiers, armed in their stings,
Make boot upon the summer's velvet buds,
Which pillage they with merry march bring home
To the tent-royal of their emperor;
Who, busied in his majesty, surveys
The singing masons building roofs of gold,
The civil citizens kneading up the honey,
The poor mechanic porters crowding in
Their heavy burdens at his narrow gate,
The sad-eyed justice, with his surly hum,
Delivering o'er to executors pale
The lazy yawning drone.

WILLIAM SHAKESPEARE
(from KING HENRY V, Act I, Scene 2)

Little City

Spider, from his flaming sleep,
staggers out into the window frame;
swings out from the red den where he slept
to nest in the gnarled glass.
Fat hero, burnished cannibal
lets down a frail ladder and ties a knot,
sways down to a landing with furry grace.

By noon this corner is a bullet-colored city
and the exhausted architect sleeps in his pale wheel,

waits without pity for a gold visitor
or coppery captive, his aerial enemies
spinning headlong down the window to the trap.

The street of string shakes now and announces
a surprised angel in the tunnel of thread,
Spider dances down his wiry heaven to taste the moth.
A little battle begins and the prison trembles.
The round spider hunches like a judge.
The wheel glistens.
But this transparent town that caves in at a breath
is paved with perfect steel.
The victim hangs by his feet, and the spider
circles invisible avenues, weaving a grave.

By evening the web is heavy with monsters,
bright constellation of wasps and bees,
breathless, surrendered.
Bronze skeletons dangle on the wires
and a thin wing flutters.
The medieval city hangs in its stars.

Spider lumbers down the web
and the city stretches with the weight of his walking.
By night we cannot see the flies' faces
and the spider, rocking.

ROBERT HORAN

In a Garden

Greenfly, it's difficult to see
Why God, who made the rose, made thee.

A. P. HERBERT

To a Louse, on Seeing One on a Lady's Bonnet at Church

Ha! whare ye gaun, ye crowlan ferlie*!
Your impudence protects you sairly:
I canna say but ye strunt rarely,
Owre gawze and lace;
Tho' faith, I fear ye dine but sparely,
On sic a place.

Ye ugly, creepan, blastet wonner,
Detested, shunn'd, by saunt an' sinner,
How daur ye set your fit upon her,
Sae fine a Lady!
Gae somewhere else and seek your dinner,
On some poor body.

Swith, in some beggar's haffet* squattle;
There ye may creep, and sprawl, and sprattle,
Wi' ither kindred, jumping cattle,
In shoals and nations;
Whare horn nor bane ne'er daur unsettle,
Your thick plantations.

Now haud you there, ye're out o' sight,
Below the fatt'rels*, snug and tight,
Na faith ye yet, ye'll no be right,
Till ye've got on it,
The vera tapmost, towrin height
O' Miss's bonnet.

My sooth! right bauld ye set your nose out,
As plump an' gray as onie grozet*:

* ferlie: wonder
* haffet: temple
* fatt'rels: folderols
* grozet: gooseberry

O for some rank, mercurial rozet*,
Or fell, red smeddum*,
I'd gie you sic a hearty dose o't,
Wad dress your droddum*!

I wad na been surpriz'd to spy
You on an auld wife's flainen* toy*;
Or aiblins* some bit duddie* boy,
On's wyliecoat*;
But Miss's fine Lunardi*, fye!
How daur ye do't?

O Jenny dinna toss your head,
An' set your beauties a' abread!
Ye little ken what cursed speed
The blastie's makin!
Thae winks and finger-ends, I dread,
Are notice takin!

O wad some Pow'r the giftie gie us
To see oursels as ithers see us!
It wad frae monie a blunder free us
An' foolish notion:
What airs in dress an' gait wad lea'e us,
And ev'n Devotion!

ROBERT BURNS

* rozet: rosin
* smeddum: powder
* droddum: breech
* flainen: flannel
* toy: old-fashioned headdress
* aiblins: maybe
* duddie: small, ragged
* wyliecoat: flannel vest
* Lunardi: balloon-bonnet

The Centipede

The centipede is not quite nice;
He lives in idleness and vice;
  He has a hundred legs.
He also has a hundred wives,
And each of these if she survives
  Has just a hundred eggs;
So that's the reason if you pick
Up any boulder, stone or brick
  You nearly always find
A swarm of centipedes concealed;
They scatter far across the field,
  But *one* remains behind.
And you may reckon then, my son,
That not alone that luckless one
  Lies pitiful and torn,
But millions more of either sex—
100 multiplied by X—
  Will never now be born;
I dare say it will make you sick,
But so does all Arithmetic.

The gardener says, I ought to add,
The centipede is not so bad;
  He rather likes the brutes.
The millipede is what he loathes;
He uses wild bucolic oaths
  Because it eats his roots;
And every gardener is agreed
That if you see a centipede
  Conversing with a milli—
On one of them you drop a stone,
The other one you leave alone—

I think that's rather silly;
They may be right, but what I say
Is "Can one stand about all day
And *count* the creature's legs?"
It has too many, any way,
And any moment it may lay
Another hundred eggs!
So if I see a thing like *this*

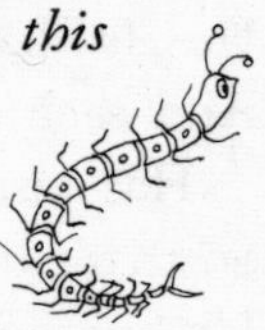

I murmur "Without prejudice,"
And knock it on the head;
And if I see a thing like *that*

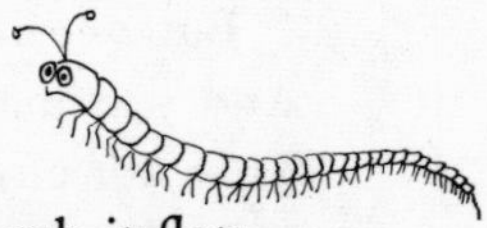

I take a brick and squash it flat;
In either case it's dead.

A. P. HERBERT

Grasshoppers

Grasshoppers go in many a thrumming spring
And now to stalks of tasselled sour-grass cling,
That shakes and swees* awhile, but still keeps straight;
While arching oxeye doubles with his weight.
Next on the cat-tail grass with farther bound
He springs, that bends until they touch the ground.

JOHN CLARE

* swees: swings

                                r-p-o-p-h-e-s-s-a-g-r
                        who
a)s w(e loo)k
upnowgath
                PPEGORHRASS
                                                eringint(o-
aThe):l
            eA
                !p:
S   a
                                (r
rIvInG   .gRrEaPsPhOs)
                                                            to
rea(be)rran(com)gi(e)ngly
,grasshopper;

E. E. CUMMINGS

A Considerable Speck

(MICROSCOPIC)

A speck that would have been beneath my sight
On any but a paper sheet so white
Set off across what I had written there.
And I had idly poised my pen in air
To stop it with a period of ink
When something strange about it made me think.
This was no dust speck by my breathing blown,
But unmistakably a living mite
With inclinations it could call its own.
It paused as with suspicion of my pen,

And then came racing wildly on again
To where my manuscript was not yet dry;
Then paused again and either drank or smelt—
With loathing, for again it turned to fly.
Plainly with an intelligence I dealt.
It seemed too tiny to have room for feet,
Yet must have had a set of them complete
To express how much it didn't want to die.
It ran with terror and with cunning crept.
It faltered; I could see it hesitate;
Then in the middle of the open sheet
Cower down in desperation to accept
Whatever I accorded it of fate.

I have none of the tenderer-than-thou
Collectivistic regimenting love
With which the modern world is being swept.
But this poor microscopic item now!
Since it was nothing I knew evil of
I let it lie there till I hope it slept.

I have a mind myself and recognize
Mind when I meet with it in any guise.
No one can know how glad I am to find
On any sheet the least display of mind.

ROBERT FROST

from *To a Butterfly*

I've watched you now a full half-hour,
Self-pois'd upon that yellow flower;
And, little Butterfly, indeed
I know not if you sleep or feed.

How motionless!—not frozen seas
More motionless; and then
What joy awaits you, when the breeze
Hath found you out among the trees,
And calls you forth again!

This plot of Orchard-ground is ours;
My trees they are, my Sister's flowers;
Here rest your wings when they are weary;
Here lodge as in a sanctuary.
Come often to us, fear no wrong;
Sit near us on the bough—
We'll talk of sunshine and of song,
And summer days when we were young;
Sweet childish days, that were as long
As twenty days are now.

WILLIAM WORDSWORTH

from *Nursery Rhymes for the Tender-hearted*

(DEDICATED TO DON MARQUIS)

Scuttle, scuttle, little roach—
How you run when I approach:
Up above the pantry shelf.
Hastening to secrete yourself.

Most adventurous of vermin,
How I wish I could determine
How you spend your hours of ease,
Perhaps reclining on the cheese.

Cook has gone, and all is dark—
Then the kitchen is your park:
In the garbage heap that she leaves
Do you browse among the tea leaves?

How delightful to suspect
All the places you have trekked:
Does your long antenna whisk its
Gentle tip across the biscuits?

Do you linger, little soul,
Drowsing in our sugar bowl?
Or, abandonment most utter,
Shake a shimmy on the butter?

Do you chant your simple tunes
Swimming in the baby's prunes?
Then, when dawn comes, do you slink
Homeward to the kitchen sink?

Timid roach, why be so shy?
We are brothers, thou and I.
In the midnight, like yourself,
I explore the pantry shelf!

CHRISTOPHER MORLEY

On the Grasshopper and Cricket

The poetry of earth is never dead:
  When all the birds are faint with the hot sun,
  And hide in cooling trees, a voice will run
From hedge to hedge about the new-mown mead;
That is the Grasshopper's—he takes the lead

In summer luxury,—he has never done
With his delights; for when tired out with fun
He rests at ease beneath some pleasant weed.
The poetry of earth is ceasing never:
On a lone winter evening, when the frost
Has wrought a silence, from the stove there shrills
The Cricket's song, in warmth increasing ever,
And seems to one in drowsiness half lost,
The Grasshopper's among some grassy hills.

JOHN KEATS

The Caterpillar

Brown and furry
Caterpillar in a hurry,
Take your walk
To the shady leaf, or stalk,
Or what not,
Which may be the chosen spot.
No toad spy you,
Hovering bird of prey pass by you;
Spin and die,
To live again a butterfly.

CHRISTINA ROSSETTI

The Cure

"I've swallowed a fly," cried Marjorie Fry.
(We could hear it buzzing inside her.)
"And I haven't a hope of getting it out
Unless I swallow a spider."

We found a web by the garden wall,
And back to the house we hurried
And offered the spider to Marjorie Fry,
Who was looking extremely worried.

"Now shut your eyelids, Marjorie Fry,
And open your wee mouth wider.
Whatever it does, the fly won't buzz
If only you'll swallow the spider."

ALFRED NOYES

Birds

Questioning Faces

The winter owl banked just in time to pass
And save herself from breaking window glass.
And her wings straining suddenly aspread
Caught color from the last of evening red
In a display of underdown and quill
To glassed-in children at the window sill.

ROBERT FROST

The Great Black Crow

The crow—the crow! the great black crow!
He cares not to meet us wherever we go;
He cares not for man, beast, friend, nor foe,
For nothing will eat him he well doth know.
  Know—know! you great black crow!
It's a comfort to feel like a great black crow!

The crow—the crow! the great black crow!
He loves the fat meadows—his taste is low;
He loves the fat worms, and he dines in a row
With fifty fine cousins all black as a sloe.
  Sloe—sloe! you great black crow!
But it's jolly to fare like a great black crow!

The crow—the crow! the great black crow!
He never gets drunk on the rain or snow;
He never gets drunk, but he never says no!
If you press him to tipple ever so.
  So—so! you great black crow!
It's an honor to soak like a great black crow!

The crow—the crow! the great black crow!
He lives for a hundred years and mo';
He lives till he dies, and he dies as slow
As the morning mists down the hill that go.
  Go—go! you great black crow!
But it's fine to live and die like a great black crow!

PHILIP JAMES BAILEY

Something Told the Wild Geese

Something told the wild geese
  It was time to go.
Though the fields lay golden,
  Something whispered, "Snow."
Leaves were green and stirring,
  Berries, luster-glossed,
But beneath warm feathers
  Something cautioned, "Frost."
All the sagging orchards
  Steamed with amber spice,
But each wild breast stiffened
  At remembered ice.
Something told the wild geese
  It was time to fly—
Summer sun was on their wings,
  Winter in their cry.

RACHEL FIELD

Life

I met four guinea hens today,
creaking like pulleys.

"A crrk," said one,
"a crrk," said two,
"a crrk," said three,
"a crrk," said four.

I agree with you cheerfully, ladies.

ALFRED KREYMBORG

The Skylark

Bird of the wilderness,
Blithesome and cumberless,
Sweet be thy matin o'er moorland and lea!
Emblem of happiness,
Blest is thy dwelling-place—
O to abide in the desert with thee!
Wild is thy lay and loud
Far in the downy cloud,
Love gives it energy, love gave it birth.
Where, on thy dewy wing,
Where art thou journeying?
Thy lay is in heaven, thy love is on earth.

O'er fell and fountain sheen,
O'er moon and mountain green,
O'er the red streamer that heralds the day,

Over the cloudlet dim,
Over the rainbow's rim,
Musical cherub, soar, singing, away!
Then, when the gloaming comes,
Low in the heather blooms,
Sweet will thy welcome and bed of love be!
Emblem of happiness,
Blest is thy dwelling-place—
O to abide in the desert with thee!

JAMES HOGG

Hurt Hawks

I

The broken pillar of the wing jags from the clotted shoulder,
The wing trails like a banner in defeat,
No more to use the sky forever but live with famine
And pain a few days: cat nor coyote
Will shorten the week of waiting for death, there is game without talons.

He stands under the oak-bush and waits
The lame feet of salvation; at night he remembers freedom
And flies in a dream, the dawns ruin it.
He is strong and pain is worse to the strong, incapacity is worse.
The curs of the day come and torment him
At distance, no one but death the redeemer will humble that head.
The intrepid readiness, the terrible eyes.
The wild God of the world is sometimes merciful to those
That ask mercy, not often to the arrogant.
You do not know him, you communal people, or you have forgotten him;

Intemperate and savage, the hawk remembers him;
Beautiful and wild, the hawks, and men that are dying remember
him.

II

I'd sooner, except the penalties, kill a man than a hawk; but the
great redtail
Had nothing left but unable misery
From the bone too shattered for mending, the wing that trailed
under his talons when he moved.
We had fed him six weeks, I gave him freedom,
He wandered over the foreland hill and returned in the evening,
asking for death,
Not like a beggar, still eyed with the old
Implacable arrogance. I gave him the lead gift in the twilight.
What fell was relaxed,
Owl-downy, soft feminine feathers; but what
Soared: the fierce rush: the night-herons by the flooded river
cried fear at its rising
Before it was quite unsheathed from reality.

ROBINSON JEFFERS

Mallard

Squawking they rise from reeds into the sun,
climbing like furies, running on blood and bone,
with wings like garden shears clipping the misty air,
four mallard, hard winged, with necks like rods
fly in perfect formation over the marsh.

Keeping their distance, gyring, not letting slip the air,
but leaping into it straight like hounds or divers,
they stretch out into the wind and sound their horns again.

Suddenly siding to a bank of air unbidden
by hand signal or morse message of command
down sky they plane, sliding like corks on a current,
designed so deftly that all air is advantage,

till, with few flaps, orderly as they left earth,
alighting among curlew they pad on mud.

REX WARNER

The Flight of Birds

The crow goes flopping on from wood to wood,
The wild duck wherries to the distant flood,
The starnels* hurry o'er in merry crowds,
And overhead whew by like hasty clouds;
The wild duck from the meadow-water plies
And dashes up the water as he flies;
The pigeon suthers* by on rapid wing,
The lark mounts upward at the call of spring.
In easy flights above the hurricane
With doubled neck high sails the noisy crane.
Whizz goes the pewit o'er the plowman's team,
With many a whew and whirl and sudden scream;
And lightly fluttering to the tree just by,
In chattering journeys whirls the noisy pie;
From bush to bush slow swees* the screaming jay,
With one harsh note of pleasure all the day.

JOHN CLARE

* starnels: starlings
* suthers: makes a rushing noise
* swees: swings

Eagles

Upon the black brow of a cliff where no life ever stirred
Alighted strong, hoary-winged eagles, grave bird upon bird.

They whetted their claws on the rock, sitting massive and glum
And loudly they called on their lately-fledged comrades to come.

How sure was the beat of their great heavy wings on the skies;
A furious strength was ablaze in their obdurate eyes.

To each new arrival their welcome was savagely clear:
"Hail, comrade! Delay not! The days we have longed for are
near!"

VASILY BASHKIN
(Translated from the Russian by BABETTE DEUTSCH)

from *Swans at Night*

Within the night, above the dark,
I heard a host upon the air,
Upon the void they made no mark,
For all that they went sailing there.

And from that host there came a cry,
A note of calling strange and high;
I heard it blown against the sky,
Till naught there seemed but it and I.

A long and lonely wraith of sound,
It floated out in distance wide,
As though it knew another bound,
A space wherein it never died.

I heard the swans, I heard the swans,
  I heard the swans that speed by night;
That ever, where the starlight wans,
  Fly on unseen within the height.

I never knew how wide the dark,
  I never knew the depth of space,
I never knew how frail a bark,
  How small is man within his place,

Not till I heard the swans go by,
  Not till I marked their haunting cry,
Not till, within the vague on high,
  I watched them pass across the sky. . . .

MARY GILMORE

O What if the Fowler?

O what if the fowler my blackbird has taken?
The roses of dawn blossom over the sea;
Awaken, my blackbird, awaken, awaken,
And sing to me out of my red fuchsia tree!

O what if the fowler my blackbird has taken?
The sun lifts his head from the lip of the sea—
Awaken, my blackbird, awaken, awaken,
And sing to me out of my red fuchsia tree!

O what if the fowler my blackbird has taken?
The mountain grows white with the birds of the sea;
But down in my garden, forsaken, forsaken,
I'll weep all the day by my red fuchsia tree.

CHARLES DALMON

The Ptarmigan

The ptarmigan is strange,
As strange as he can be;
Never sits on ptelephone poles
Or roosts upon a ptree.
And the way he ptakes pto spelling
Is the strangest thing pto me.

ANONYMOUS

The Throstle

"Summer is coming, summer is coming,
  I know it, I know it, I know it.
Light again, leaf again, life again, love again!"
  Yes, my wild little Poet.

Sing the new year in under the blue,
  Last year you sang it as gladly.
"New, new, new, new!" Is it then *so* new
  That you should carol so madly?

"Love again, song again, nest again, young again,"—
  Never a prophet so crazy!
And hardly a daisy as yet, little friend;
  See, there is hardly a daisy.

"Here again, here, here, here, happy year!"
  O warble unchidden, unbidden!
Summer is coming, is coming, my dear,
  And all the winters are hidden.

ALFRED, LORD TENNYSON

The Sandhill Crane

Whenever the days are cool and clear
The sandhill crane goes walking
Across the field by the flashing weir
Slowly, solemnly stalking.
The litte frogs in the tules hear
And jump for their lives when he comes near,
The minnows scuttle away in fear,
When the sandhill crane goes walking.

The field folk know if he comes that way,
Slowly, solemnly stalking,
There is danger and death in the least delay
When the sandhill crane goes walking.
The chipmunks stop in the midst of their play,
The gophers hide in their holes away
And hush, oh, hush! the field mice say,
When the sandhill crane goes walking.

MARY AUSTIN

Chain

I was chopping wood when I heard it, wild and clear
across the daring interval of snow
like the cry of a newborn child. The axe fell
from my hand. The echoes cracked within my ear like ice
before the wind. I put my snowshoes on
and started out. It took an hour to find him—
a loon, his foot half off, his eyes bleared
with pain. I drew the steel jaws apart.

He slid to the ground. His wings shuddered twice,
and were still. I raised him up, thinking of the warmth
within. His beak fastened like a vice. My cry
rang out in silver links across the dark,
and echoed on the lake, the hills, the wind.

PAUL PETRIE

Robin Redbreast

(ROBIN GOCH)

Welcome Robin with thy greeting,
On the threshold meekly waiting,
To the children's home now enter,
From the cold and snow of winter,
From the cold and snow of winter.

Art thou cold? or art thou hungry?
Pretty Robin, don't be angry,
All the children round thee rally,
While the snow is in the valley,
While the snow is in the valley.

Come in Robin, do not fear us,
Thy bright eye and chirping cheer us;
Thy sad notes excite our pity,
Now the frost begins to bite thee,
Now the frost begins to bite thee.

Robin come and tell thy story,
Leave outside thy care and worry;
Tell the children, Robin dearest,
Of the babies in the forest,
Of the babies in the forest.

Of the flame that burnt thy bosom,
Of thy wand'rings far and lonesome,
Of thy home among the greenwood,
Of thy happy days of childhood,
Of thy happy days of childhood.

WELSH FOLK SONG

The Cuckoo

Repeat that, repeat,
Cuckoo, bird, and open ear wells, heart-springs, delightfully sweet,
With a ballad, with a ballad, a rebound
Off trundled timber and scoops of the hillside ground, hollow
  hollow hollow ground:
The whole landscape flushes on a sudden at a sound.

GERARD MANLEY HOPKINS

The Snowy Owl

Eating the songbird, does it eat
The song, too? Relish it with the smack and
Tang of sauce, or wine, upon the tongue?
Little creatures, keep out of the wide purview
Of the hunting glance of the snowy owl,
Come soaring out of the north, half-starved, for you.
It is the particular owl of
Your worst nightmare; most bright,
Most terrible eye of the air
To fall afoul of.

ERNEST KROLL

A Dead Bird

Finding the feathers of a bird
Killed by a sparrow-hawk,
I thought, What need is there to walk?
And bound them on my feet;
And as I flew off through the air,
I saw men stare up from a street
And women clasp their hands in prayer.
"To Hades" was no sooner said
Than a winged Hermes I was there;
And though I peered round for the dead,
Nothing I saw and nothing heard
But a low moaning from a bough,
"Ah, who is wearing my poor feathers now?"

ANDREW YOUNG

The Swallows

All day—when early morning shone
With every dewdrop its own dawn
And when cockchafers were abroad
Hurtling like missiles that had lost their road—

The swallows twisting here and there
Round unseen corners of the air
Upstream and down so quickly passed
I wondered that their shadows flew as fast.

They steeple-chased over the bridge
And dropped down to a drowning midge

Sharing the river with the fish,
Although the air itself was their chief dish.

Blue-winged snowballs! until they turned
And then with ruddy breasts they burned;
All in one instant everywhere,
Jugglers with their own bodies in the air.

ANDREW YOUNG

crazy jay blue)
demon laughshriek
ing at me
your scorn of easily

hatred of timid
& loathing for(dull all
regular righteous
comfortable)unworlds

thief crook cynic
(swimfloatdrifting
fragment of heaven)
trickstervillain

raucous rogue &
vivid voltaire
you beautiful anarchist
(i salute thee

E. E. CUMMINGS

Whippoorwill

I've only seen him
Once in my life
And I'm bound to say
He's the ugliest bird
You'd wish to know.
He has whiskers that grow
All around his face
And his ugly shape
Is such a disgrace
That during the day
He hides away
Out of everyone's sight;
But in the night
When you lie in bed
And the moon comes up
Over the hill
And rides the sky
Above your head
You can hear him crying,
"Whip poor Will,
Whip poor Will,"
On and on and on until
You're almost crazy.
A very odd creature—
Take your choice—
A bird, or a voice?

MARY BRITTON MILLER

The Hunter

The hunter crouches in his blind
'Neath camouflage of every kind,
And conjures up a quacking noise
To lend allure to his decoys.
This grown-up man, with pluck and luck,
Is hoping to outwit a duck.

OGDEN NASH

Peacock and Nightingale

Look at the eyes look from my tail!
What other eyes could look so well?
A peacock asks a nightingale.

And how my feathers twist the sun!
Confess that no one, no, no one
Has ever seen such color spun.

Who would not fall in ecstasy
Before the gemmed enamelry
Of ruby-topaz-sapphire me?

When my proud tail parades its fan,
You, little bird, are merely an
Anachronism in its van.
Let me advise that you be wise,
Avoid the vision of my eyes.
And then the nightingale replies.

ROBERT FINCH

A Living

A bird
picks up its seeds or little snails
between heedless earth and heaven
in heedlessness.

But, the plucky little sport, it gives to life
song, and chirruping, gay feathers, fluff-shadowed warmth
and all the unspeakable charm of birds hopping and fluttering
  and being birds,
—And we, we get it all from them for nothing.

D. H. LAWRENCE

The Herons on Bo Island

The herons on Bo Island
  Stand solemnly all day;
Like lean old men together
  They hump their shoulders grey.
Oh, I wish I could get near them
  To hear the things they say!

They turn up their coat collars
  And stand so gloomily;
And somehow, as I watch them,
  It always seems to me
That in their trouser pockets
  Their wrinkled hands must be.

But if I venture near them
   They look at me in doubt,
And with great wings loose-flapping
   They circle round about,
Their long legs hanging downwards,
   Their slim necks all stretched out.

If I stood on Bo Island
   As gloomily as they,
And ruffled up my collar
   And hid my hands away,
It might be they would join me
   And I'd hear the things they say.

ELIZABETH SHANE

Song

Old Adam, the carrion crow,
   The old crow of Cairo;
He sat in the shower, and let it flow
Under his tail and over his crest;
      And through every feather
      Leaked the wet weather;
And the bough swung under his nest;
For his beak it was heavy with marrow.
   Is that the wind dying? O no;
   It's only two devils, that blow
   Through a murderer's bones, to and fro,
      In the ghosts' moonshine.

Ho! Eve, my grey carrion wife,
   When we have supped on king's marrow,
Where shall we drink and make merry our life?
Our nest it is queen Cleopatra's skull,
      'Tis cloven and cracked,

And battered and hacked,
But with tears of blue eyes it is full:
Let us drink then, my raven of Cairo.
Is that the wind dying? O no;
It's only two devils, that blow
Through a murderer's bones, to and fro,
In the ghosts' moonshine.

THOMAS LOVELL BEDDOES

The Blinded Bird

So zestfully canst thou sing?
And all this mighty indignity,
With God's consent, on thee!
Blinded ere yet a-wing
By the red-hot needle thou,
I stand and wonder how
So zestfully thou canst sing!

Resenting not such wrong,
Thy grievous pain forgot,
Eternal dark thy lot,
Groping thy whole life long,
After that stab of fire;
Enjailed in pitiless wire;
Resenting not such wrong!

Who hath charity? This bird,
Who suffereth long and is kind,
Is not provoked, though blind
And alive ensepulchred?
Who hopeth, endureth all things?
Who thinketh no evil, but sings?
Who is divine? This bird.

THOMAS HARDY

The Hummingbird

I do not see the hummingbird
that once whirred in the tangle
of cedar and woodbine and peach,
thrusting curved bill into the fragrant tubelets.
Shining green it was, color of mermaid scales,
its crimson throat a darting blossom.
It could stand still in air gathering honey,
small copter, it could fly backward and forward.
It did not mind my being near
but added an extra circle and swoop
in its erratic flight to astonish me.
Such a little thing
to leave so much emptiness.

MARY KENNEDY

Song

I had a dove, and the sweet dove died;
  And I have thought it died of grieving:
O, what could it grieve for? its feet were tied
  With a single thread of my own hand's weaving;
Sweet little red feet, why should you die—
Why should you leave me, sweet bird, why?
You lived alone in the forest tree,
Why, pretty thing! would you not live with me?
I kiss'd you oft and gave you white peas;
Why not live sweetly, as in the green trees?

JOHN KEATS

The Cuckoo

The cuckoo is a pretty bird,
  She singeth as she flies;
She bringeth us good tidings,
  She telleth us no lies;
She sucketh all sweet flowers
  To keep her throttle clear,
And every time she singeth
Cuckoo-cuckoo-cuckoo!
  The summer draweth near.

The cuckoo is a giddy bird,
  No other is as she,
That flits across the meadow,
  That sings in every tree.
A nest she never buildeth,
  A vagrant she doth roam;
Her music is but tearful—
Cuckoo-cuckoo-cuckoo!
  "I nowhere have a home."

The cuckoo is a witty bird,
  Arriving with the spring.
When summer suns are waning,
  She spreadeth wide her wing.
She flies th' approaching winter,
  She hates the rain and snow;
Like her, I would be singing,
Cuckoo-cuckoo-cuckoo!
  And off with her I'd go!

ANONYMOUS

Yellow Flutterings

Sometimes goldfinches one by one will drop
From low hung branches; little space they stop;
But sip and twitter, and their feathers sleek;
Then off at once, as in a wanton freak:
Or perhaps, to show their black, and golden wings,
Pausing upon their yellow flutterings.

JOHN KEATS

Owls Talking

I think that many owls say *Who-o:*
At least the owls that I know do-o.
But somewhere when some owls do not-t,
Perhaps they cry *Which-h, Why-y,* or *What-t.*
Or when they itch-h
They just say *Which-h,*
Or close one eye-e
And try *What-t Why-y.*

DAVID MCCORD

Bobwhite

Through hottest days the bobwhite sings;
His two-toned, reedy whistle rings
Windblown, familiar on this lawn,
Or to remoter green withdrawn,
At one with evening as with dawn.

His other name, the quail, suggests
Gunshot and slaughter-emptied nests;
The squinting eye, the flabby grin,
As the curst hunter closes in.

Bobwhite—I call him what he calls
Himself, though often he'll repeat
The first of his cool syllables
As though to quench the summer heat—
Small sun-defier, to whose golden
Note my summer is beholden.

ROBERT HILLYER

A Blackbird Singing

It seems wrong that out of this bird,
Black, bold, a suggestion of dark
Places about it, there yet should come
Such rich music, as though the notes'
Ore were changed to a rare metal
At one touch of that bright bill.

You have heard it often, alone at your desk
In a green April, your mind drawn
Away from its work by sweet disturbance
Of the mild evening outside your room.

A slow singer, but loading each phrase
With history's overtones, love, joy
And grief learned by his dark tribe
In other orchards and passed on
Instinctively as they are now,
But fresh always with new tears.

R. S. THOMAS

I Heard a Bird Sing

I heard a bird sing
 In the dark of December
A magical thing
 And sweet to remember.
"We are nearer to Spring
 Than we were in September,"
I heard a bird sing
 In the dark of December.

OLIVER HERFORD

Upon the Lark and the Fowler

 Thou simple bird what mak'st thou here to play?
Look, there's the Fowler, prethee come away.
Dost not behold the Net? Look there 'tis spread,
Venture a little further thou art dead.
 Is there not room enough in all the Field
For thee to play in, but thou needs must yield
To the deceitful glitt'ring of a Glass,
Placed twixt Nets to bring thy death to pass?
 Bird, if thou art so much for dazling light,
Look, there's the Sun above thee, dart upright.
Thy nature is to soar up to the Sky
Why wilt thou come down to the nets, and dye?
 Take no heed to the Fowler's tempting Call;
This whistle he enchanteth Birds withal.
Or if thou seest a live Bird in his net
Believe she's there 'cause thence she cannot get.
Look how he tempteth thee with his Decoy

That he may rob thee of thy Life, thy Joy:
Come, prethee, Bird, I prethee come away,
Why should this net thee take when 'scape thou may?
  Hadst thou not wings, or were thy feathers pulled,
Or wast thou blind, or fast asleep wer't lulled:
The case would somewhat alter, but for thee
Thy eyes are ope, and thou hast Wings to see.
  Remember that thy Song is in thy Rise,
Not in thy Fall, Earth's not thy Paradise.
Keep up aloft then, let thy circuits be
Above, where Birds from Fowlers nets are free. . . .

JOHN BUNYAN

Jenny Wren

Her sight is short, she comes quite near;
A foot to me's a mile to her;
And she is known as Jenny Wren,
The smallest bird in England. When
I heard that little bird at first,
Methought her frame would surely burst
With earnest song. Oft had I seen
Her running under leaves so green,
Or in the grass when fresh and wet,
As though her wings she would forget.
And seeing this, I said to her—
"My pretty runner, you prefer
To be a thing to run unheard
Through leaves and grass, and not a bird!"
'Twas then she burst, to prove me wrong,
Into a sudden storm of song,
So very loud and earnest, I
Feared she would break her heart and die.

"Nay, nay," I laughed, "be you no thing
To run unheard, sweet scold, but sing!
O I could hear your voice near me,
Above the din in that oak tree,
When almost all the twigs on top
Had starlings singing without stop."

W. H. DAVIES

Water Ouzel

Misunderstood and largely mispronounced,
The water ouzel, youzel be advised,
Dives into mountain streams, fresh air renounced,
And *walks* along the bottom. You surprised?

DAVID MCCORD

Some Brown Sparrows

Some brown sparrows who live
in the Bronx Zoo visit often
the captive Victoria Crested
Pheasant, visit captive Peacocks,
Cockatoos. They fly through bars
to visit also monkeys, jackals,
bears. They delouse themselves in
cage dust, shaking joyously;
they hunt for bread crumbs, seeds
or other tidbits. Briefly,
they lead free sparrow lives
and fly free.

BRUCE FEARING

The Heron

The heron stands in water where the swamp
Has deepened to the blackness of a pool,
Or balances with one leg on a hump
Of marsh grass heaped above a musk-rat hole.

He walks the shallow with an antic grace.
The great feet break the ridges of the sand,
The long eye notes the minnow's hiding place.
His beak is quicker than a human hand.

He jerks a frog across his bony lip,
Then points his heavy bill above the wood.
The wide wings flap but once to lift him up.
A single ripple starts from where he stood.

THEODORE ROETHKE

Vespers

O Blackbird, what a boy you are!
How you do go it!
Blowing your bugle to that one sweet star—
How you do blow it!
And does she hear you, blackbird boy, so far?
Or is it wasted breath?
"Good Lord! she is so bright
To-night!"
The blackbird saith.

T. E. BROWN

The Eagle

He clasps the crag with crooked hands;
Close to the sun in lonely lands,
Ringed with the azure world, he stands.
The wrinkled sea beneath him crawls;
He watches from his mountain walls,
And like a thunderbolt he falls.

ALFRED, LORD TENNYSON

Watching Bird

Deep in the marsh and dappled woods
I saw a thrush's staring eye:
Part of the brush and undershades,
He watched me come there like a spy.

The eye deep brown and ringed with white
Beheld me standing out of place
In shadow, seeming no way right,
Least of all, motionless a space.

He perched low on a rotten stump,
He cocked an eye and took my time:
Cones from the pines made slide and thump
From green height to the bottom slime.

Had I not moved, I still would stay
Stared out of countenance, a fool
Who looked-at shall not look away,
Foundered and covert in a pool.

LOUIS O. COXE

Blue Jay

All the flowers are sleeping,
A feather blanket of snow
Over them.
Blue Jay balances on a dry old sunflower's bent head . . .
He dives under . . .
He strikes out seeds with angry beak.
His wings are barred with frost.
His snow-dusty feet
Are like dull crystal.
I like him . . . almost . . .
But must he keep on screeching in such a voice
And the flowers at their wits' end
For a little quiet?

HILDA CONKLING, age 11

Sea Gull

The sea gull curves his wings,
the sea gull turns his eyes.
Get down into the water, fish!
(if you are wise.)

The sea gull slants his wings,
the sea gull turns his head.
Get deep into the water, fish!
(or you'll be dead.)

ELIZABETH COATSWORTH

The Owl

In the hollow tree, in the old gray tower,
 The spectral owl doth dwell;
Dull, hated, despised, in the sunshine hour,
 But at dusk he's abroad and well!
Not a bird of the forest e'er mates with him;
 All mock him outright by day;
But at night, when the woods grow still and dim,
 The boldest will shrink away!
 O, when the night falls, and roosts the fowls,
 Then, then, is the joy of the hornèd owl!

And the owl hath a bride, who is fond and bold,
 And loveth the wood's deep gloom;
And with eyes like the shine of the moonstone cold,
 She awaiteth her ghastly groom;
Not a feather she moves, not a carol she sings,
 As she waits in her tree so still;
But when her heart heareth his flapping wings,
 She hoots out her welcome shrill!
 O, when the moon shines, and dogs do howl,
 Then, then, is the joy of the hornèd owl!

Mourn not for the owl, nor his gloomy plight!
 The owl hath his share of good:
If a prisoner he be in the broad daylight,
 He is lord in the dark greenwood!
Nor lonely the bird, nor his ghastly mate,
 They are each unto each a pride;
Thrice fonder, perhaps, since a strange, dark fate
 Hath rent them from all beside!
So, when the night falls, and dogs do howl,

Sing, ho! for the reign of the hornèd owl!
We know not alway
Who are kings by day,
But the king of the night is the bold brown owl!

BRYAN W. PROCTER (BARRY CORNWALL)

Robert of Lincoln

Merrily swinging on brier and weed,
Near to the nest of his little dame,
Over the mountain-side or mead,
Robert of Lincoln is telling his name:
Bob-o'-link, bob-o'-link,
Spink, spank, spink;
Snug and safe is that nest of ours,
Hidden among the summer flowers.
Chee, chee, chee.

Robert of Lincoln is gayly dressed,
Wearing a bright black wedding-coat;
White are his shoulders and white his crest.
Hear him call in his merry note:
Bob-o'-link, bob-o'-link,
Spink, spank, spink;
Look, what a nice new coat is mine,
Sure there was never a bird so fine.
Chee, chee, chee.

Robert of Lincoln's Quaker wife,
Pretty and quiet, with plain brown wings,
Passing at home a patient life,
Broods in the grass while her husband sings:
Bob-o'-link, bob-o'-link,
Spink, spank, spink;
Brood, kind creature, you need not fear
Thieves and robbers while I am here.
Chee, chee, chee.

Modest and shy as a nun is she;
One weak chirp is her only note.
Braggart and prince of braggarts is he,
Pouring boasts from his little throat:
Bob-o'-link, bob-o'-link,
Spink, spank, spink;
Never was I afraid of man;
Catch me, cowardly knaves, if you can!
Chee, chee, chee.

Six white eggs on a bed of hay,
Flecked with purple, a pretty sight!
There as the mother sits all day,
Robert is singing with all his might:
Bob-o'-link, bob-o'-link,
Spink, spank, spink;

Nice good wife, that never goes out,
Keeping house while I frolic about.
Chee, chee, chee.

Soon as the little ones chip the shell,
Six wide mouths are open for food;
Robert of Lincoln bestirs him well,
Gathering seeds for the hungry brood.
Bob-o'-link, bob-o'-link,
Spink, spank, spink;
This new life is likely to be
Hard for a gay young fellow like me.
Chee, chee, chee.

Robert of Lincoln at length is made
Sober with work, and silent with care;
Off his holiday garment laid,
Half forgotten that merry air;
Bob-o'-link, bob-o'-link,
Spink, spank, spink;
Nobody knows but my mate and I
Where our nest and our nestlings lie.
Chee, chee, chee.

Summer wanes; the children are grown;
Fun and frolic no more he knows;
Robert of Lincoln's a humdrum crone;
Off he flies, and we sing as he goes:
Bob-o'-link, bob-o'-link,
Spink, spank, spink;
When you can pipe that merry old strain,
Robert of Lincoln, come back again.
Chee, chee, chee.

WILLIAM CULLEN BRYANT

The Hoopee

The hoopee is a nasty bird
And always has been such.
And that is why nice people
Have never liked him much.

JOHN BECKER

Answer to a Child's Question

Do you ask what the birds say? The Sparrow, the Dove,
The Linnet and Thrush say, "I love and I love!"
In the winter they're silent—the wind is so strong;
What it says, I don't know, but it sings a loud song.
But green leaves, and blossoms, and sunny warm weather,
And singing, and loving—all come back together.
But the Lark is so brimful of gladness and love,
The green fields below him, the blue sky above,
That he sings, and he sings; and for ever sings he—
"I love my Love, and my Love loves me!"

SAMUEL TAYLOR COLERIDGE

The Ostrich

The ostrich roams the great Sahara.
Its mouth is wide, its neck is narra.
It has such long and lofty legs,
I'm glad it sits to lay its eggs.

OGDEN NASH

from *Truth*

The self-applauding bird, the peacock, see—
Mark what a sumptuous pharisee is he!
Meridian sunbeams tempt him to unfold
His radiant glories; azure, green, and gold:
He treads as if, some solemn music near,
His measur'd step were govern'd by his ear;
And seems to say—Ye meaner fowl, give place:
I am all splendour, dignity, and grace!

WILLIAM COWPER

A Bird Came Down the Walk

A bird came down the walk:
He did not know I saw;
He bit an angle-worm in halves
And ate the fellow, raw.

And then he drank a dew
From a convenient grass,
And then hopped sidewise to the wall
To let a beetle pass.

He glanced with rapid eyes
That hurried all abroad—
They looked like frightened beads, I thought
He stirred his velvet head

Like one in danger; cautious,
I offered him a crumb,

And he unrolled his feathers
And rowed him softer home

Than oars divide the ocean,
Too silver for a seam,
Or butterflies, off banks of noon,
Leap, plashless, as they swim.

EMILY DICKINSON

Stupidity Street

I saw with open eyes
Singing birds sweet
Sold in the shops
For the people to eat,
Sold in the shops of
Stupidity Street.

I saw in a vision
The worm in the wheat,
And in the shops nothing
For people to eat:
Nothing for sale in
Stupidity Street.

RALPH HODGSON

Animals All Together

Animals

I think I could turn and live with animals, they are so placid and self-contained;
I stand and look at them long and long.
They do not sweat and whine about their condition;
They do not lie awake in the dark and weep for their sins;
They do not make me sick discussing their duty to God;
Not one is dissatisfied—not one is demented with the mania of owning things;
Not one kneels to another, nor to his kind that lived thousands of years ago;
Not one is respectable or industrious over the whole earth.

WALT WHITMAN

Old Noah's Ark

Old Noah once he built an ark,
And patched it up with hickory bark.
He anchored it to a great big rock,
And then he began to load his stock.
The animals went in one by one,
The elephant chewing a carroway bun.
The animals went in two by two,
The crocodile and the kangaroo.

The animals went in three by three,
The tall giraffe and the tiny flea,
The animals went in four by four,
The hippopotamus stuck in the door.
The animals went in five by five,
The bees mistook the bear for a hive.
The animals went in six by six,
The monkey was up to his usual tricks.
The animals went in seven by seven,
Said the ant to the elephant, "Who're ye shov'n?"
The animals went in eight by eight,
Some were early and some were late.
The animals went in nine by nine,
They all formed fours and marched in a line.
The animals went in ten by ten,
If you want any more, you can read it again.

FOLK RHYME

Old Friends

Oh, sure am I when come to die,
And through Death's portals go,
Those cats, and dogs, and little white mice,
And birds, I used to know,
Shall all come rushing to welcome me,
Their friend of the long ago.

And the cats will purr, "We've missed you, sir,
And we know you missed us too."
And the dogs will bark, "Good morning, friend,
We've waited long for you."
And the little white mice shall squeak with joy,
And the birds will chirp and coo.

And happen what may on the Judgement Day,
I shall not affrighted be,
If the cats and dogs, and all weak dumb things
That on earth were dear to see,
Should receive from God the gift of speech,
For I know that they'll plead for me.

A. MUIR

Tit for Tat

Have you been catching of fish, Tom Noddy?
Have you snared a weeping hare?
Have you whistled, "No Nunny," and gunned a poor bunny,
Or a blinded bird of the air?

Have you trod like a murderer through the green woods,
Through the dewy deep dingles and glooms,
While every small creature screamed shrill to Dame Nature,
"He comes—and he comes!"?

Wonder I very much do, Tom Noddy,
If ever, when you are a-roam,
An Ogre from space will stoop a lean face,
And lug you home:

Lug you home over his fence, Tom Noddy,
Of thorn-stocks nine yards high,
With your bent knees strung around his old iron gun
And your head dan-dangling by:

And hang you up stiff on a hook, Tom Noddy,
From a stone-cold pantry shelf,
Whence your eyes will glare in an empty stare,
Till you are cooked yourself!

WALTER DE LA MARE

from *Song of Myself*

I am afoot with my vision:
Where the panther walks to and fro on a limb overhead, where
the buck turns furiously at the hunter,
Where the rattlesnake suns his flabby length on a rock, where the
otter is feeding on fish,
Where the alligator in his tough pimples sleeps by the bayou,
Where the black bear is searching for roots or honey, where the
beaver pats the mud with his paddle-shaped tail;
Where the quail is whistling betwixt the woods and the wheat-lot,
Where the bat flies in the Seventh-month eve, where the great
gold-bug drops through the dark,
Where cattle stand and shake away flies with the tremulous
shuddering of their hides,
Where the she-whale swims with her calf and never forsakes it,
Where the fin of the shark cuts like a black chip out of the water,
Where the heifers browse, where geese nip their food with short
jerks,
Where sun-down shadows lengthen over the limitless and
lonesome prairie,
Where herds of buffalo make a crawling spread of the square
miles far and near,
Where the humming-bird shimmers, where the neck of the
long-lived swan is curving and winding,
Where the laughing-gull scoots by the shore, where she laughs
her near-human laugh,
Where bee-hives range on a grey bench in the garden half hid by
the high weeds,
Where band-neck'd partridges roost in a ring on the ground with
their heads out,
Where winter wolves bark amid wastes of snow and icicled trees,
Where the yellow-crowned heron comes to the edge of the marsh
at night and feeds upon small crabs—

Pleas'd with the native, and pleas'd with the foreign, pleas'd
with the new and the old . . .
I tramp a perpetual journey (come listen all!) . . .
Not I, not anyone else can travel that road for you,
You must travel it for yourself.

WALT WHITMAN

Pets

Once we had a little retriever
But it bit our beaver
Which had already bitten
Our Siamese kitten
Which had not been pleasant
To our golden pheasant.
The pheasant took a dislike to Laura,
Our Angora,
Who left her hairs
On the Louis Quinze chairs
And her paws
On one of our jackdaws
Who were not at all nice
To our white mice
Who were openly rude
To our bantam brood
Whose beaks were too sharp
For our golden carp
Who were on rotten terms
With our silk-worms
Who were swallowed up
By our retriever pup
Who consequently died
With all that silk inside.

Then we knew we'd have to buy
Something so high
And stout and strong it
Would let nobody wrong it;
So we purchased a Hyena
Which, though it ate my sister Lena
And some embroidery off the shelf,
Remained intact itself
And has not yet died
So that our choice was justified.

DANIEL PETTIWARD

short course in natural history

the patagonian
penguin
is a most
peculiar
bird
he lives on
pussy
willows
and his tongue
is always furred
the porcupine
of chile
sleeps his life away
and that is how
the needles
get into the hay
the argentinian
oyster
is a very
subtle pink

for when he s
being eaten
he pretends he is
a skink
when you see
a sea gull
sitting
on a bald man s dome
she likely thinks
she s nesting
on her rocky
island home
do not tease
the inmates
when strolling
through the zoo
for they have
their finer feelings
the same
as me and you
oh deride not
the camel
if grief should
make him die
his ghost will come
to haunt you
with tears
in either eye
and the spirit of
a camel
in the midnight gloom
can be so very
cheerless
as it wanders
round the room

archy

DON MARQUIS

from *Auguries of Innocence*

. . . To see the World in a grain of sand,
And a Heaven in a wild flower,
Hold Infinity in the palm of your hand,
And Eternity in an hour.
A robin redbreast in a cage
Puts all Heaven in a rage.
A dove-house fill'd with doves and pigeons
Shudders Hell thro' all its regions.
A dog starv'd at his master's gate
Predicts the ruin of the State.
A horse misus'd upon the road
Calls to Heaven for human blood.
Each outcry of the hunted hare
A fibre from the brain does tear.
A skylark wounded in the wing,
A cherubim does cease to sing.
The game-cock clipt and arm'd for fight
Does the rising sun affright.
Every wolf's and lion's howl
Raises from Hell a Human soul.
The wild deer, wandering here and there,
Keeps the Human soul from care.

The lamb misus'd breeds public strife
And yet forgives the butcher's knife.
The bat that flits at close of eve
Has left the brain that won't believe.
The owl that calls upon the night
Speaks the unbeliever's fright.
He who shall hurt the little wren
Shall never be belov'd by men.
He who the ox to wrath has mov'd
Shall never be by woman lov'd.
The wanton boy that kills the fly
Shall feel the spider's enmity.
He who torments the chafer's sprite
Weaves a bower in endless night.
The caterpillar on the leaf
Repeats to thee thy mother's grief.
Kill not the moth nor butterfly,
For the Last Judgement draweth nigh.
He who shall train the horse to war
Shall never pass the polar bar.
The beggar's dog and widow's cat,
Feed them, and thou wilt grow fat.

WILLIAM BLAKE

Ballade of a Zoo Buff

The zoo is a wonderful place;
  I'm happy to say it with feeling.
No animal's nature is base;
  The puma is very appealing.
  A day with the apes is revealing;
They rather suggest me to you;
  A stay with the hippos is healing—
I never get bored at the zoo.

The jaguar is girded with grace;
  Have *you* seen an elephant kneeling?
The seals set a scintillant pace;
  The rhesuses swing from the ceiling.
  The finches like swooping and wheeling;
The tones of the civet and gnu
  Are purer than temple-bells pealing—
I never get bored at the zoo.

There isn't the tiniest trace
  Of double or quadruple dealing;
The crocodile has a sweet face—
  Would *he* think of cheating or stealing?
  The polar bear dreams of congealing
And I dream while watching him, too,
  But this I'd not dream of concealing:
I never get bored at the zoo.

MILTON BRACKER

The Bells of Heaven

'Twould ring the bells of Heaven
The wildest peal for years,
If Parson lost his senses
And the people came to theirs,
And he and they together
Knelt down with angry prayers
For tamed and shabby tigers
And dancing dogs and bears,
And wretched, blind pit ponies,
And little hunted hares.

RALPH HODGSON

Impossible Animals

Let No One Suppose

Let no one suppose
That the creatures he knows—
The robin, the rat,
The cat on the mat,
The toad in his hole,
The vole and the mole,
The hog and the dog,
The fat, freckled frog,
The fish in the seas
And the birds in the trees,
The beasts in the Zoo,
The paunched kangaroo,
The swan on the lake,
The serpent or snake,
The ant, the ant-eater,
The chimp and the cheetah—
Let no one suppose that creatures like those
Are A L L that the Animal Kingdom can show:

NO!

When the woods rumble low
And storm-clouds ride by in the purplish sky,
At the corners of dreams,
Round the edges of sleep,
There's a something that seems to be going to creep,
To crawl or to climb, to lumber or leap

Round the corners of dreams and the edges of sleep.
You cannot be sure that you fastened the door,
You cannot be certain that under the curtain
There isn't a tail or a paw or a claw.
And what makes you wonder is never the thunder
Nor wind in the chimney nor rain on the tiles,
It *must* be—
PREFABULOUS ANIMILES!

So if any suppose
That the creatures he knows
In pond or in park,
By daylight and dark,
Are all that the Animal Kingdom contains,
Then some day he'll see them lurking in lanes,
Or breaking down hedges and fences and stiles—
He'll *see* the Prefabulous Animiles.

JAMES REEVES

song from *James and the Giant Peach*

"We may see a Creature with forty-nine heads
Who lives in the desolate snow,
And whenever he catches a cold (which he dreads)
He has forty-nine noses to blow.

"We may see the venomous Pink-Spotted Scrunch
Who can chew up a man with one bite.
It likes to eat five of them roasted for lunch
And eighteen for its supper at night.

"We may see a Dragon, and nobody knows
That we won't see a Unicorn there.

We may see a terrible Monster with toes
Growing out of the tufts of his hair.

"We may see the sweet little Biddy-Bright Hen
So playful, so kind and well-bred;
And such beautiful eggs! You just boil them and then
They explode and they blow off your head.

"A Gnu and a Gnocerous surely you'll see
And that gnormous and gnorrible Gnat
Whose sting when it stings you goes in at the knee
And comes out through the top of your hat.

"We may even get lost and be frozen by frost.
We may die in an earthquake or tremor.
Or nastier still, we may even be tossed
On the horns of a furious Dilemma.

"But who cares! Let us go from this horrible hill!
Let us roll! Let us bowl! Let us plunge!
Let's go rolling and bowling and spinning until
We're away from old Spiker and Sponge!"

ROALD DAHL

Not Me

The Slithergadee has crawled out of the sea.
He may catch all the others, but he won't catch me.
No you won't catch me, old Slithergadee,
You may catch all the others, but you wo—

SHELLEY SILVERSTEIN

The Doze

Through Dangly Woods the aimless Doze
A-dripping and a-dribbling goes.
His company no beast enjoys.
He makes a sort of hopeless noise
Between a snuffle and a snort.
His hair is neither long nor short;
His tail gets caught on briars and bushes,
As through the undergrowth he pushes.
His ears are big, but not much use.
He lives on blackberries and juice

And anything that he can get.
His feet are clumsy, wide and wet,
Slip-slopping through the bog and heather
All in the wild and weepy weather.
His young are many, and maltreat him;
But only hungry creatures eat him.
He pokes about in mossy holes,
Disturbing sleepless mice and moles,
And what he wants he never knows—
The damp, despised, and aimless Doze.

JAMES REEVES

The Unicorn

The Unicorn stood, like a king in a dream,
On the bank of a dark Senegambian stream;
And flaming flamingoes flew over his head,
As the African sun rose in purple and red.

Who knows what the thoughts of a unicorn are
When he shines on the world like a visiting star;
When he comes from the magical pages of story
In the pride of his horn and a halo of glory?

He followed the paths where the jungle beasts go,
And he walked with a step that was stately and slow;
But he threw not a shadow and made not a sound,
And his foot was as light as the wind on the ground.

The lion looked up with his terrible eyes,
And growled like the thunder to hide his surprise.
He thought for a while, with a paw in the air;
Then tucked up his tail and turned into his lair.

The gentle giraffe ran away to relate
The news to his tawny and elegant mate,
While the snake slid aside with a venomous hiss,
And the little birds piped: "There is something amiss!"

But the Unicorn strode with his head in a cloud
And uttered his innocent fancies aloud.
"What a wonderful world!" he was heard to exclaim;
"It is better than books: it is sweeter than fame!"

And he gazed at himself, with a thrill and a quiver,
Reflected in white by the slow-flowing river:
"Oh, speak to me, dark Senegambian stream,
And prove that my beauty is more than a dream!"

He had paused for a word in the midst of his pride,
When a whisper came down through the leaves at his side
From a spying, malevolent imp of an ape
With a twist in his tail and a villainous shape:

"He was made by the stroke of a fanciful pen;
He was wholly invented by ignorant men.

One word in his ear, and one puff of the truth—
And a unicorn fades in the flower of his youth."

The Unicorn heard, and the demon of doubt
Crept into his heart, and the sun was put out.
He looked in the water, but saw not a gleam
In the slow-flowing deep Senegambian stream.

He turned to the woods, and his shadowy form
Was seen through the trees like the moon in a storm.
And the darkness fell down on the Gambian plain;
And the stars of the Senegal sought him in vain.

He had come like a beautiful melody heard
When the strings of the fiddle are tunefully stirred;
And he passed where the splendors of melody go
When the hand of the fiddler surrenders the bow.

E. V. RIEU

The Sea Serpant

AN ACCURATE DESCRIPTION

A-sleepin' at length on the sand,
   Where the beach was all tidy and clean,
A-strokin' his scale with the brush on his tail
   The wily Sea Serpant I seen.

And what was his color? you asks,
   And how did he look? inquires you,
I'll be busted and blessed if he didn't look jest
   Like you would of expected 'im to!

His head was the size of a—well,
The size what they always attains;
He whistled a tune what was built like a prune,
And his tail was the shape o' his brains.

His scales they was ruther—you know—
Like the leaves what you pick off of eggs;
And the way o' his walk—well, it's useless to talk,
For o'course you've seen Sea Serpants' legs.

His length it was seventeen miles,
Or fathoms, or inches, or feet
(Me memory's sich that I can't recall which,
Though at figgers I've seldom been beat).

And I says as I looks at the beast,
"He reminds me o'somethin' I've seen—
Is it candy or cats or humans or hats,
Or Fenimore Cooper I mean?"

And as I debated the point,
In a way that I can't understand,
The Sea Serpant he disappeared in the sea
And walked through the ocean by land.

And somehow I knowed he'd come back,
So I marked off the place with me cap;
'Twas Latitude West and Longitude North
And forty-eight cents by the map.

And his length it was seventeen miles,
Or inches, or fathoms, or feet
(Me memory's sich that I can't recall which,
Though at figgers I've seldom been beat).

WALLACE IRWIN

When the Sline Comes to Dine

When the Glub-Toothed Sline
Comes to my house to dine,
You may find me in France or Detroit
Or off in Khartoum,
Or in the spare room
Of my Uncle Ed's place in Beloit.

You may call me in Philly,
Racine or Rabat.
You may reach me in Malmö or Ghor.
You may see me in Paris,
And likely as not,
You will run into me at the store.

You may find me in Hamburg,
Or up in Saint Paul,
In Kyoto, Kenosha or Gnome.
But one thing is sure,
If you find me at all,
You *never* shall find me at home.

SHELLEY SILVERSTEIN

The Catipoce

"O Harry, Harry! hold me close—
I fear some animile.
It is the horny Catipoce
With her outrageous smile!"

Thus spoke the maiden in alarm;
   She had good cause to fear:
The Catipoce can do great harm,
   If any come too near.

Despite her looks, do not presume
   The creature's ways are mild;
For many have gone mad on whom
   The Catipoce has smiled.

She lurks in woods at close of day
   Among the toadstools soft,
Or sprawls on musty sacks and hay
   In cellar, barn, or loft.

Behind neglected rubbish-dumps
   At dusk your blood will freeze
Only to glimpse her horny humps
   And hear her fatal sneeze.

Run, Run! adventurous boy or girl—
   Run home, and do not pause
To feel her breath around you curl,
   And tempt her carrion claws.

Avoid her face: for underneath
   That gentle, fond grimace
Lie four-and-forty crooked teeth—
   My dears, avoid her face!

"O Harry, Harry! hold me close,
   And hold me close a while;
It is the odious Catipoce
   With her devouring smile!"

JAMES REEVES

The Horny-Goloch

The horny-goloch is an awesome beast,
Soople and scaly;
It has twa horns, and a hantle* o' feet,
And a forky tailie.

ANONYMOUS

About the Bloath

In the undergrowth
There dwells the Bloath
Who feeds upon poets and tea.
Luckily I know this about him,
While he knows almost nothing of me.

SHELLEY SILVERSTEIN

The Centaurs

Playing upon the hill three centaurs were!
They lifted each a hoof! They stared at me!
And stamped the dust!

They stamped the dust! They snuffed upon the air!
And all their movements had the fierce glee
Of power, and pride, and lust!

* hantle: a great many

Of power and pride and lust! Then, with a shout,
They tossed their heads, and wheeled, and galloped round,
In furious brotherhood!

In furious brotherhood! Around, about,
They charged, they swerved, they leaped! Then, bound on bound,
They raced into the wood!

JAMES STEPHENS

The Nonny

The Nonny-bird I love particularly;
All day she chirps her joysome odes.
She rises perpendicularly,
And if she goes too far, explodes.

JAMES REEVES

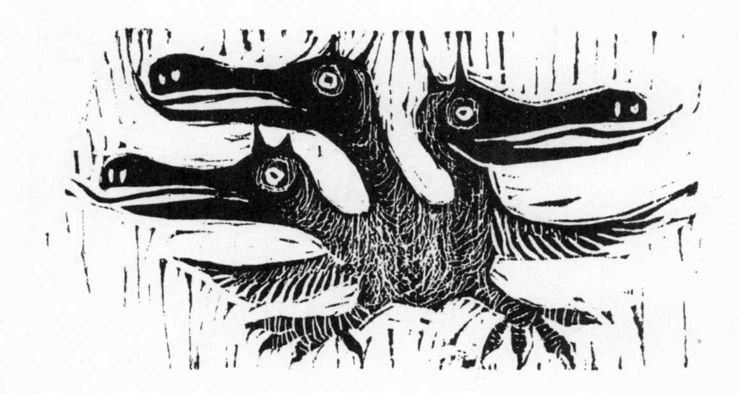

Author index

Title index

4 5 67